A History of Navigation
in the Royal Air Force

RAF Historical Society Seminar at the
RAF Museum, Hendon
21 October 1996

(Held jointly with The Royal Institute of Navigation and
The Guild of Air Pilots and Air Navigators)

The opinions expressed in this publication are those of the authors concerned and are not necessarily those held by the Royal Air Force Historical Society.

Copyright © 1997 Royal Air Force Historical Society

First published in the UK in 1997 by the
Royal Air Force Historical Society

British Library Cataloguing in Publication Data available

ISBN 0 9519824 7 8

Typeset and printed in Great Britain by Fotodirect Ltd, Brighton

Royal Air Force Historical Society

Contents

Illustrations

From left to right: Alec Ayliffe, 'Jeff' Jefford, Sir John Curtiss, Philip Saxon, David Page

From left to right: David Broughton, Jack Furner, Sir John Curtiss, Norman Bonnor, Bill Tyack

1. Welcoming Address
by Air Vice-Marshal Nigel Baldwin
Chairman of the Royal Air Force
Historical Society

Good morning, Ladies and Gentlemen. My name is Nigel Baldwin; as the relatively newly elected Chairman of the RAF Historical Society, this is the first time I have had the privilege of welcoming you to an all-day seminar. A special welcome, of course, to the members of the Royal Institute of Navigation (who have provided half of the speakers) and to the Guild of Air Pilots and Air Navigators. Walter Blanchard, President of the RIN, and Ron Bridge, Master-Elect of GAPAN, will be called on to say a few words later in the proceedings.

This is the first such joint meeting that the Historical Society has held, and it comes at an apposite time. Ten years ago yesterday, Professor R. V. Jones addressed the founder members at their first meeting. We have now grown to around 650. Today's attendance has broken all records for the Hendon seminars and, as always, I would like immediately to put on record our appreciation to Dr Fopp and his Museum colleagues for allowing us to use their splendid facilities.

Doubtless like our sister organisations, we are always seeking new members: in the reception area there is information about all three bodies. There is already a deal of cross-membership, but we are very happy to encourage more.

Also in the reception area, British Aerospace have provided a fascinating display of the most up-to-date navigation systems: and we are grateful for that.

So to today. Nobody is better qualified to guide us through the day than Sir John Curtiss. First of all he is a navigator with an RAF career that spanned just about all the Commands, beginning with Bomber Command in 1944. He commanded Bruggen in the early 70's: he was

Commandant at Bracknell, and the Senior Air Commander at Northwood during the Falklands War in 1982. He retired as AOC 18 Group, and has spent much of the subsequent years as Director and Chief Executive of the Society of British Aerospace Companies. Sir John, it gives me great pleasure, as a pilot, to say to you, as a navigator, – "You have control".

Royal Air Force Museum Lecture Hall – Air Navigation Seminar

2. *Introductory Remarks by the Seminar Chairman Air Marshal Sir John Curtiss*

Thank you, Chairman, very much indeed. Right, on with the proceedings.

The invention of the aeroplane by itself was, of course, just the first step. If the aircraft was going to be of any use and to take Man where he wanted to go, he had to be able to take it to the right place at the right time and over the shortest distance; and thus the art of aerial navigation was developed.

Very similar problems had faced Mankind countless years before. Having designed ships that could cross oceans, Man set out to explore the World and to exploit the lands that he found. Polynesians, for example, like those who crossed the Pacific to colonise 'Aotea-roa', or New Zealand as it is now known, used the stars to guide them although, like so many of the ancient mariners, they had no certainty as to their precise position or, indeed, where they were going. Centuries later navigation at sea was still an uncertain art, and countless ships and many thousands of sailors came to an untimely end because no-one knew how to measure longitude accurately.

It was, in fact, not until 1713 when the Government of the day set the prize for the discovery at the then very princely sum of £20,000 that enormous energy was applied to solving the problem. Although it was well understood that an accurate time keeping clock was the key, no-one at that time knew how to construct one. Many theories were advanced: some were bizarre, if not simply lunatic. The one that I think must appeal to all navigators was the 'wounded dog' theory, put forward in 1687. This was predicated on a quack miraculous cure called 'the powder of sympathy', which could heal at a distance. All one had to do to release the magic was to apply the powder to an article from an ailing patient. It was not, however, painless; so the theory postulated that by placing a dog with an unhealed wound on board a ship, and retaining a used bandage back at base and then applying the powder to that bandage at precisely 12 noon each day the dog would yelp, thus disclosing the precise Greenwich Time! Sadly, I recall no such marvellous nostrums for position-finding when I was doing my navigation training. However, the longitude problem was solved in the middle of the 18th century when John Harrison patented an accurate chronometer for use at sea for the first time, and even then, I am sad to say, the Longitude Committee managed to cheat him out of a large proportion of his prize.

Turning back to this century and to the conquest of the air, it is really quite astonishing that in the course of the lifetime of many of us here today aerial navigation has run a complete course from road maps and binoculars to instant and accurate positioning to within a few feet anywhere in the world; or out of it for that matter.

Now to tell you this fascinating story we have assembled a small team of expert protagonists who, between them, have some 232 years of service. They are led by Philip Saxon who conceived, developed and has arranged this day's Seminar, and to whom we owe an enormous debt of gratitude. But before introducing the first speaker, may I just remind you that we are running a very tight schedule here today and that timing is of the essence: – not, I hope, a difficult concept for the navigators amongst us. But we must have a full discussion period at the end of both the morning and afternoon sessions, so I do ask that we try to keep to time: and to give a good example of this I think that I have managed to steal about seven minutes by cutting my introduction short.

3.   The Early Years

Mr David Page

Chairman's Introduction:

So to start the proceedings and to explain the link between marine and aerial navigation, we have David Page. He is a Master Mariner as well as a Fellow of the Royal Institute of Navigation. He spent twelve years with the Merchant Navy before doing his flying training with the Royal Navy. He then transferred to civil aviation and, by 1959, was Chief Navigator for British Caledonian Airways. He has played an important role within both the CAA and the ICAO, serving among other things on the Future Air Navigation Systems Committee; and he is currently Chairman of the RIN Technical Committee.

I had some reservations when the Historical Society invited me to talk to this Seminar on the early years of air navigation. I have not had the privilege of serving in the Royal Air Force having been a Merchant Seaman and Naval Reservist who learnt to fly with the Royal Navy and who subsequently opted for a career in Civil Aviation. However, as a member of the Royal Institute of Navigation's History of Air Navigation Group I was aware of the part played in the early development of air navigation by the dark blue types, in particular the old-style RNR's, the former Merchant Seamen. The proposed date settled matter. Today is of course Trafalgar Day!

Some historical papers start with the statement that in the beginning there were pilots – only pilots. This is not strictly true. Balloons had been used for military observation purposes long before the Wright Brothers and thus the observer pre-dated the pilot by at least half a century. In Britain a military balloon factory, later to become the RAE Farnborough, had been established at Chatham in 1882. Consequently people were considering the requirements for aeronautical maps or charts well before 1903. By 1907, a year before the first heavier than air flight in Britain, an International Commission for Aeronautical Charts had been established in Brussels. The first specialised air map to appear in Britain was produced by Clift and Gross for the 1912 Aerial Derby.

Thus in the same year that the Flying Corps, with Naval and

Military Wings, was established by Royal Warrant the provision of one of the basic navigational requirements, suitable maps and charts, was already in hand.

1912 was a vintage year in other ways. During the Army's summer manoeuvres on Salisbury Plain aircraft were used successfully for reconnaissance. (One of the observers being a certain Major Trenchard). The value of aircraft for reconnaissance, a task previously carried out by cavalry, was demonstrated and it was principally in this role that the RFC accompanied the British Expeditionary Force in 1914, the first operational reconnaissance flights being carried out over Belgium for the BEF on the 19th August by a Bleriot, flown by Capt. Philip Joubert, and a BE 2C.

As the conflict in France ground into trench warfare the RFC settled down to the task of assisting the Army with long and short range reconnaissance, photographic reconnaissance, mapping, artillery spotting and the first attempts as strategic bombing. The terms long and short range need some clarification in this context. An "Army Wing" responsible for long range activities would have a front of about ten miles and its aerodromes would be within thirty miles of the front line and its area of operation would extend about the same distance into enemy territory. A "Corps Wing" concentrating on short range activities, such as artillery co-operation would only have a front of 5,000 yards.

Thus even the so-called long range activities took place in a very limited area and given good visibility, once crews were familiar with the terrain and local landmarks, navigation was not a significant problem. In such circumstances even an accurate compass was hardly essential, general orientation was probably adequate.

The aircraft of the day were equipped with air-speed indicators and altimeters and the need for corrections for height and temperature had been appreciated at an early stage. The development of a really satisfactory aircraft compass took longer, although British compass development seems to have kept well ahead of that of the enemy judging by the reports of compasses taken from crashed British aircraft being found in German aircraft. The problem of northerly turning error was not fully understood until the work of Keith Lucas at Farnborough in 1917.

Most of the "tools" for air navigation were available at that time. There were drift sights, course and distance calculators, hand-bearing compasses, plotting boards and even that old friend the Douglas Protractor. The theory was nothing new – the mariners had been using it for many years and it was well documented. Had the RFC found that poor navigation was significantly affecting operations it seems logical to suppose that the appropriate actions would have been taken. This view is supported by the fact that when, in late 1917, the RFC began to use its obsolete FE 2b fighters as night bombers additional navigational training was deemed necessary. Also, when in 1918 it was planned to bomb Berlin with the Handley Page 0/400, in answer to the Zeppelin and Gotha raids on London, a technique of fixing by taking radio bearings was envisaged and the four-man crews were to be specially trained at Andover. The Armistice brought about an end to these plans and so it is not surprising that the Air Publication of 1920 "Notes on Air Pilotage" only considered the navigation of short flights over mist and cloud, at night and up to a hundred miles over the sea.

In comparison the naval wing of the RFC, which became the RNAS under the control of the Admiralty in July 1914, had to be more concerned with navigation from the very nature of its tasks. Although the Royal Naval Air Service was initially responsible for air defence of Great Britain, the RFC being fully occupied in France, its main concerns were maritime reconnaissance and anti-submarine and anti-Zeppelin patrols over the sea.

The RNAS was also not slow to engage in strategic bombing as shown by the pioneering raid by Avro 504's on the Zeppelin sheds at Friedrichshafen. This raid required a certain navigational capability but it was the over-water tasks which really dictated navigational requirements. The navigation section of the November 1914 Naval Air Service Training Manual may sound a trifle quaint today but the basic principles are there. In addition the majority of the crews, at least in the early days, had a sound basic knowledge of navigation which the Regulars of the Executive Branch needed for their watch-keeping certificates and which had been hammered into them from the age of thirteen. The Reservists, of which there were a consider-able number, possibly because aviation did not appeal to many career-conscious Regulars, were often Merchant Service Officers and experienced navigators. For example, the first course of ten Naval Officers to graduate from the Central Flying School at Upavon in April 1913 contained four reservists, with a Lt. F. Bowhill RNR, a

Master Mariner who was later to become Air Marshal Sir Frederick at the top of the list. Another Reservist Lt E L Johnson, later navigator of the R100 and the R101 and possibly the leading air navigator of his time, had left his tramp ship for the Navy and was operating SS Airships in 1916. (Delving in the records it was thus no surprise to find the former Second Officer of the Titanic flying as the Observer of a Short 184, operating from the seaplane carrier Campania with the Grand Fleet at Scapa.)

With the commencement of hostilities in 1914 there was a need for over-water navigation which increased with time. Six days after the invasion of Belgium two Naval Airships were escorting Transports on the short sea crossing to France, not unduly demanding in a navigational sense, but remaining airborne for about twelve hours. One of them, HMA No. 4, was under the command of Lt G H Scott (later to take the R 34 to New York and back).

By 1917 Scott was in command of HMA No 9 on North Sea Patrols which covered greater distances. On one of these the airship was underway for 26hrs 45mins. Even the later versions of the smaller Coastal Class, non-rigid, airships had a cruising endurance of 24 hours.

The airships were, of course, only a part of the Naval Air Services's strength. On the 1 April 1918, when the RAF was established, the RNAS had 2,949 aircraft and 103 airships. Within the aircraft strength there were a large number of seaplanes and flying boats employed on coastal and North Sea patrols all of which needed varying degrees of navigational capability to be effective. There were the Short 184 seaplanes which served at every coastal air station and in every theatre of the war. With about a three hour endurance the 184 has the distinction of being the first aircraft to sink a ship with a torpedo. There were the Curtiss H 12 and H 16 flying boats with at least a six hour endurance together with, probably the most successful, the Felixstowe F 2A boats some of which stayed airborne for nine and a half hours. It was these flying boats which operated the historic "Spiders Web" patrol system over the southern part of the North Sea.

There is little evidence in the records of any serious concern regarding the navigation of these over-water operations. As the Service expanded rapidly there were complaints regarding the ability of some Midshipmen posted as Observers in seaplanes but this would appear to have been a question of inexperience coupled with the well known fact that each new generation of midshipmen is never as good as the last.

There were, of course, individual instances of navigational difficulties – the third Handley Page Bomber allocated to the RNAS was delivered intact to the enemy due to a navigation error – but in general terms the standard of navigation would seem to have been on a par with that of the smaller ships in the Fleet. Neither the open bridges of small warships or the open cockpits of aircraft provided a comfortable or convenient navigation station. As early as 1913 Winston Churchill, then First Lord of the Admiralty, wrote that "The safe navigation of airships is a difficult problem, but there is little doubt that navigation appliances will be developed as has been done for water ships". He then went on to mention the development of bubble sextants and directional radio systems for use in the air. In the same year he also wrote to the Second Sea Lord about entry to the Naval Air Wing "We need not worry too much about educational tests. What is needed for this dangerous service is a young gentleman and a good animal".

While the latter statement may be debatable Winston's forecast for the future of air navigation has proved to be correct.

In 1919 the Royal Air Force held a five month advanced navigation course at the School of Air Pilotage at Andover and some of the officers from this course were then used as instructors for the first "Long N" course at the newly formed School of Aerial Navigation and Naval Co-operation at Calshot. This course was of twelve months duration and the instructing staff were almost all ex-RNAS; the Chief Instructor (Squadron Leader G G H Cooke) had navigated the R 34 on her double crossing of the Atlantic. There were ten students who had been selected by competitive examination. The first steps in the development of radio direction-finding and radar had already been taken, almost two decades earlier, around the time the first aeroplane flew. It could well have been claimed that a good foundation had been laid for future navigational excellence. But twenty years later only five per cent of the bombs dropped were within five miles of the target and only one in four Coastal Command aircraft managed to find its convoy. What went wrong?

There were, of course, exceptions. The Special Operations Flights into occupied Europe, the Swordfish minelaying in harbour approaches or the Maryland flight in appalling weather conditions which confirmed that Bismark had left Grimstad Fjord, all demonstrated considerable navigational competence and I am sure that there are other examples but the fact remains that the overall standard of navigation was not as it should have been.

I would suggest that the frequent demands for economy during the inter-war years ensured that the Service retained only a small number of experienced navigation specialists who, in any case, did not have sufficient seniority to influence the decision making process. It is also possible that those who did control policy during the inter-war years were guided by their own experience with the RFC in France during WWI and did not fully appreciate the future requirement.

I look forward to hearing the views of the next speaker.

SOURCES

The Author is grateful for advice from Wg Cdr C G Jefford and for a preview of his paper *"The Observer in the British Air Services, 1914-1918."*

Holmes R. *Riding the Retreat.* 1995

Hughes A J. *History of Air Navigation.* 1946

Johnston Gp Capt E A. *Airship Navigator.* 1994

Navy Records Society. *Papers relating to the RNAS.*

Saxon Sqn Ldr P H. *The Development of Specialist Navigation Training in the Royal Air Force.*

4.   RAF Navigation Between the Wars

Flight Lieutenant Alec Ayliffe

Chairman's Introduction:

You are quite right about the seniority of navigators: I remember when the War ended in 1945, the most senior man wearing a navigator's brevet to gain a permanent commission was as a Squadron Leader . . . Right, we now turn to our second presentation which will be given by Flight Lieutenant Alec Ayliffe, who joined the RAF in 1975 after reading Modern History at Oxford. He completed tours on the Shackleton and the Nimrod, and with the Central Trials and Tactics Organisation. He recently held an appointment with the Military Survey Defence Agency, where he was responsible for processing digital geographic information for the RAF; and he is now at Boscombe Down as a Missions System Trials Officer . . . Alec . . .

INTRODUCTION

"I was, incidentally, astonished by the complacency that existed regarding our ability to navigate at long range by night."

This assessment on RAF attitudes to air navigation at the start of the Second World War was written by Professor R V Jones[1] with the benefit of hindsight. Whilst the use of hindsight is appropriate to examine the decisions of those paid to exercise foresight, it can hinder the understanding of past events. The historical perception of RAF navigation in the years between the wars is one of failure; the previous speaker, David Page has asked us what went wrong? Clearly, in the light of Bomber Command's difficulties with navigation in the Second World War, as revealed by the Butt Report[2], it is difficult to argue that RAF navigational development was a great achievement but, in the context of the time, real, if limited, progress was made.

The late Group Captain F C "Dickie" Richardson, whose notes and memoirs are the principle source for this paper[3], played a significant role in improving the standards of RAF navigators. He certainly believed that the Air Board had neglected navigation, but he would feel aggrieved if the work of the few enthusiasts, who did so much to develop a core of expertise and navigational competence in the RAF before the Second World War, was not properly acknowledged. Concentration on these few individuals would, however, give the wrong impression of RAF navigation. It must be remembered that the years between the wars were in a pioneering age. Airmen flew in open cockpits with no radios. If an airman was lost, or uncertain of his position, he could often land and ask the way. Navigation did not seem difficult or important to most RAF pilots, who flew by day and in good weather. Perhaps it could be said that nothing seemed difficult or important to RAF pilots, for there was a spirit in the pre-war RAF which, although it cannot be captured in words, must be acknowledged if we are to understand the attitude to navigation which prevailed[4]. The RAF was a dedicated and professional organisation, but pilots were prepared to operate at and beyond the limits imposed by available equipment and knowledge.

This paper intends to provide only a brief account of the practice and development in RAF navigation before the war. Important subjects, such as the development of compasses and the blind flying panel, can only be mentioned in passing. Specific ground-breaking flights will also be ignored, although Wing Commander Jefford will discuss some of the epic flights of the period. Beginning with comments on some of the historical writings which reinforce the impression of navigational neglect by the RAF, the paper will attempt to put this historical view into a broader context of RAF history. The paper will review the state of RAF navigation in 1918 and then provide an account of its practice and the development of its theory before 1939. Of course, lessons are often learnt from hard experience and a few navigational mishaps will be mentioned, if only because these misfortunes led to a concerted effort to improve navigation training. The limited nature of the progress over these 21 years is illustrated by examining the state of RAF navigation in 1939. Finally, the paper concludes with some thoughts on the relationship of navigation to the broader implementation of RAF dogma and the development of Air Power.

THE HISTORICAL VIEW

Most histories of the RAF before the war ignore navigation[5]. It is only with the hindsight of the Second World War that navigation was seen to be important for the RAF. As an official historian writing shortly after the War, Denis Richards could not ignore documented criticism of RAF navigation preparedness, but he put a gloss on the problem, and on other related problems, such as the lack of bomb development, as a rare instance of lack of foresight. Richards noted that:

"Except in the coastal reconnaissance squadrons and the few squadrons with the primary role of night bombing, there had been too little attention to long distance navigation and blind flying."[6]

The official history was quick to add to this mild criticism that, in general, the RAF of 1939 had up-to-date equipment, sound organisation, correct principles and, above all, was well-staffed and well led.

As unofficial historians writing with the benefit of time, John Terraine, in *The Right of the Line*[7] and Max Hastings in *Bomber Command*[8] discuss the problem of navigation in the RAF in depth. Both Terraine and Hastings use reports written by the AOC of Bomber Command from 1937-1940, Air Chief Marshal Sir Edgar Ludlow-Hewitt, to show that the neglect of navigation was critical. The irony is that Ludlow-Hewitt was one of the strongest critics of an aircrew trade dedicated to, and responsible for, aircraft navigation. It is also noteworthy that Professor Jones' comment on complacency is quoted by Max Hastings, who is one of the severest critics of the pre-war RAF.

None of these historians explains how the RAF could have developed better navigation methods at the time, although radio aids are occasionally mentioned. Sir Maurice Dean points out in his study, "The Royal Air Force and Two World Wars", that before 1936, there had been little incentive to develop expensive navigation aids and training at a time when the RAF was battling for its survival[9]. Official policy, not formally abandoned until February 1933[10], ruled that Britain would not fight a war for ten years. Scientific and technical revolutions do not occur spontaneously, and before the RAF began to expand there would be no widespread demand or motivation to improve navigation in the RAF. In addition, it should be noted that, as Correlli Barnett has argued[11], Britain had very limited technical and intellectual resources on which to base a revolution in electronics or navigation.

At the end of the Second World War, when major advances had been made in all aspects of air navigation, there was no sympathy with these arguments. The few enthusiasts who had seen themselves as prophets in the wilderness before 1939 meant to reinforce their victory, and to do this they inadvertently criticised their own achievements. The Director of Navigation and Control at the Air Ministry gave a lecture on "Developments in Air Navigation" to No. 16 War Course at RAF Staff College. The following précis of the part of this lecture dealing with the period 1918 to 1939 provides a useful summary of what was to become the historical view:

> "**Technique.** Remained static during this period and followed principles evolved during the 1914-1918 War. Little attempt made to forecast the requirements of a future war nor to develop navigation practice and tactics to meet such requirements.
>
> **Instruments.** Apart from improvements to aircraft compasses and maps for air use, design and production of navigating instruments did not receive adequate attention. Example: the Navigation Staff at Air Ministry stated that the Air Position Indicator and an Integrating Sextant were known requirements, yet neither of these instruments was produced until the War was well advanced (1942) . . .
>
> **Training.** Prior to 1936, navigation training, except for pilots destined for flying boat squadrons, was spasmodic and ineffective. A few officers were admitted to a short navigation course in which the majority failed to take any great interest; while specialist training catered for only **two** officers a year!
>
> **General.** Policy of "laissez faire" seems to have been adopted towards air navigation matters during this period. Thus in September 1939 the navigation effort of the RAF was sustained only by adequate compasses and maps and an unbounded optimism in the infallibility of the method of following a railway line to the target."[12]

This is the view that seems to have prevailed.

RAF NAVIGATION IN 1918

As David Page has mentioned, by the end of the First World War, air navigation was well understood. In 1915 an air navigation manual could be published with scant regard to the effects of drift; by 1917 the standard text book written by Commander Bosanquet and

Lieutenant Commander Campbell showed a solid understanding of all elements of air navigation. Most notably, this manual includes a comprehensive account of compass errors, which is not surprising owing to Campbell's work at the Admiralty Compass Observatory. The development of the Aperiodic Compass in Britain was a significant advance which made Dead Reckoning possible. Other instruments had also been improved and particular problems of Air Navigation, as opposed to Marine Navigation, were identified.

Some First World War developments were to remain in use for most of the period up to the Second World War. One device, a mechanical computer called the Course and Distance Calculator, which was based on a naval instrument, remained particularly popular in the British Empire. The Course and Distance Calculator was used to calculate the effects of the wind on an aircraft's flight and remained in service into the late 30s when it was replaced by a new generation of DR computers, which are, with some modification, still in service today. Plotting aids, such as the Bigsworth chart board and Douglas protractor were also introduced[13]. Finally, an instrument had been created at Farnborough to measure the angle between aircraft heading and its track (the "drift" angle) by observing the aircraft's progress over the surface.

The development of air navigation had been remarkable, but it should not lead to the conclusion that the application of new techniques had taken deep root in the RAF. Navigation was an activity for specialists. One of the key individuals in the development of navigational instruments at Farnborough had been Major H E Wimperis, who had a drift and bomb sight named after him. It is interesting to note that Wimperis read a paper to the Royal Aeronautical Society in April 1919 which had the title "Air Navigation: The Most Important of the Unsolved Problems Relating to Aviation". Wimperis certainly believed that there was much work still to be done, but by this time he had become a mere technical specialist[14]. However, after the Armistice, the reduction in defence spending and cuts in the RAF hindered any further progress.

One result of the demobilisation was the end of the Observer trade. In 1918 some observers, particularly those from the RNAS, had effectively become dedicated and trained aircraft navigators. Despite opposition from some senior pilots, Ludlow-Hewitt and Trenchard amongst others, the career prospects and status of this new generation of aircrew had even seemed assured. However, the observers quickly vanished from the RAF and it was not until 1937 that the idea of the observer as navigator was reinstated, and even then the trade was given a more lowly status than it had in 1918[15]. As well as discarding the observer trade, the RAF lost many of its pilot navigators immediately after the war. The rapid expansion of navigation training units at the end of the war turned into an abrupt reduction. One unit to survive was the School of Air Pilotage (quickly renamed to the Air Pilotage School to avoid the acronym SOAP) at Andover. This school ran one course in 1919; with postings and demobilisation taking its toll on both staff and students, only 16 of 38 students ended the course, 4 of whom were classed as failed. Interestingly, a Squadron Leader Arthur Harris passed out top of the Course.

THE PRACTICE OF AIR NAVIGATION

The need for Air Navigation had not been a high priority for much of the Royal Flying Corps element of the RAF. Most flights were conducted over land in fair weather and map-reading seemed adequately to fulfil the requirements of getting to the right place. The relevant Air Publication, AP44, "Notes on Air Pilotage", published in July 1920, did envisage short flights over mist and cloud, at night and up to 100 miles over the sea; but the use of the term Air Pilotage to designate the basic navigation to be used when in sight of landmarks for most of the flight implies an acknowledgement that air navigation was something special. In practice, if pilots got lost they would find a suitable place, land and ask the way. This was perfectly feasible then, as even the largest aircraft was made of "stick and string" and could be landed in an average grass field.

Navigation, as practised by most pilots, was an art requiring a knowledge of railway lines, rather than of meteorology and trigonometry. "Bradshawing", so named from the British railway timetable, was accepted as a good way of following the right route. Even out in the North Sea there were plenty of Lightships, buoys and coastal shipping to show the way. In the outposts of Empire, visibility was usually good. Pilots, sitting in open cockpits goggled and wearing "Bombay Bowlers", navigated over varied terrain equipped with rudimentary instruments and a library of topographical maps on a scale 1:1 million, cut to foolscap, pasted and over-varnished on to thin plywood boards. Most aircraft had little room for anything more elaborate than a Bigsworth Chart Board. The approach to navigation was practical and entirely suited to the nature of the flying machines of the day. For example, rudimentary tables of drift against wind, airspeed and relative heading were published for those not inclined to use the Course and Distance Calculator[16].

A most impressive example of this practical approach, was the creation of the Cairo to Baghdad Air Mail route[17]. This route took some time to prepare and obtaining the funds was, as might be expected, one of the major difficulties. Navigation over the feature-less Syrian desert between Amman and Rutbah Wells in Iraq presented much less of a problem. The idea of creating landmarks at one mile intervals with explosives was not, however, pursued and instead, after a land survey, a very useful deep furrow was ploughed straight across the otherwise featureless terrain. The creation of emergency landing grounds was an equally important preparation for this air route which became an important element of colonial infra-structure. It should be noted that the use of lighthouses at night or of Wireless DF stations and any other luxuries or "infrastructure" would have aggravated the funding problems and almost certainly prevented the successful creation of this route.

There were, of course, a number of flights undertaken by the RAF which required considerable navigation expertise, but these will be discussed by Wing Commander Jefford separately. One area of air navigation expertise which should be mentioned, was in the airship fleet, but this had little impact on the development of navigation in the RAF, although one of the greatest Air Navigators of the day Squadron Leader E L Johnston, an airship navigator who had retired from the RAF shortly after the war, made a major contribution to the profes-sion and, as the first Deputy Master, to the Guild of Air Pilots and Air Navigators. It should also be noted that the seaplane squadrons were serious practitioners of air navigation out of sight of the land. Even the operations of coastal aircraft were severely limited by poor weather. However, it was at Calshot, the home of seaplane navigation, that knowledge of navigation was maintained at a high level.

THE DEVELOPMENT OF NAVIGATION

The navigation school at Calshot was not responsible for the develop-ment of navigation, but since there was no other authority to direct navigational progress, it inevitably became the centre for initiating improvements in navigation. The Royal Aircraft Establishment (RAE) at Farnborough did play a major part in developing instruments and equipment, but it was a very small establishment and its work proceeded very slowly. The Admiralty Compass Observatory (ACO) also worked on improving direct indicating compasses, so that by 1939 the British "dead beat" compasses were undoubtedly the best in the world. However, the development of air navigation was an international and remarkably open activity. Progress was not dramatic, but there were steady improvements in instruments and techniques. These improvements are well documented in the many air navigation manuals published between the wars. By the 1930s these books were mainly intended for use by civil pilots aspiring to a professional licence. The RAF navigation "Bible" AP1234, The Manual of Air Navigation part 1, revised in 1935, was aimed firmly at the coastal pilot, but is typical of the high standard of many of these text books. AP 1234 has 19 chapters including substantial discussions devoted to maps and charts, navigational instruments, aircraft compasses and compass adjustment, Direction Finding Wireless Telegraphy and Meteorology. Significantly, the last chapter is devoted to Ground Organisation and such essential elements as "Notices to Airmen" and the "Air Pilot".

Commercial interest in Air Navigation led to a proliferation of instruments and ideas. The most notable figures in this enterprise were, perhaps, Lieutenant Commander Philip Weems of the United States Navy, who founded the Weems System of Navigation[18], and A J Hughes, of Henry Hughes and Sons[19], a well-known maker of navigation instruments. These men served to publicise developments in navigation and corresponded with many of the main air navigation practitioners around the world. Hughes even published Weems' best selling text book in a British Empire edition which took care to exclude some sections on instruments produced by competitors in the U.S. Weems corresponded with several RAF navigation specialists and was an agent in ensuring that RAF theory of navigation remained up to date.

One of Weems' interests was in DR calculators. The wide variety of these instruments, particularly those developed by Dalton was not well publicised around the British Empire. However, by 1939 the RAF Pattern Course and Distance Calculator which resembled some of these American devices, was beginning to replace the First World

War model. A circular slide rule, first proposed by Appleyard in the First War, was still placed on the rear of the calculator, although its calibration was to an International Commission of Air Navigation (ICAN) scale.

Weems' most significant interest was in Astronomical Navigation, or astro, and he had exploited a plotting system of Star Curves similar in concept to the Baker Navigating Machine used by Brown on the crossing of the Atlantic. There were many attempts to simplify the over complex procedures of the marine navigator for airborne use. Donald Bennett was particularly fond of the Bygrave position line slide-rule which could be operated in simple steps. Weems, however, was the main advocate of an Air Almanac and, abandoning graphical methods of sight reduction, became a firm proponent of sight reduction tables. Hughes, who had a long term interest in the sale of sextants, organised meetings between Weems and interested RAF officers in 1935 and 1936. As a result the RAF became converted to the idea of an Air Almanac and the use of sight reduction tables. A special trial course was held in 1937 to decide whether the use of astro was practicable for general use in the RAF. In November 1937 the CAS formally endorsed the decision to make astro a standard navigation procedure for General Reconnaissance and Twin-Engine Bomber pilots. Astro navigation was extensively covered by AP 1456, Volume II of the Manual of Air Navigation, which was written by Kelly Barnes, one of the most forceful advocates of a distinct air navigation profession, and issued in 1938. It is notable that this book refers to tables expected to be published in 1942.

Critical to the development of astro was, of course, the development of a satisfactory sextant. A wide variety of sextants for use in aircraft were created before 1939, including the well known RAE bubble sextants. It had quickly become established after 1919, that an artificial horizon was a necessity for airborne astro and the bubble chamber became the favoured means of supplying this reference. By the 1930s, the problem of compensating for acceleration errors had led to much controversy and research into methods of averaging readings to compensate for large errors. Despite the commercial incentive to be first to market, progress was slow. The standard issue RAF sextant of 1939, the Mk IX, did not have an automatic averaging device. More interesting, given the RAF's commitment to astro, was that only in 1939 was Weems informed by one of his correspondents that compensation should be made for acceleration errors due to the rotation of the earth. Correction for Coriolis, or "Z" as it became known, is in the order of 2 to 3 miles to the right of track at speeds of around 100 to 150 knots at 50°N and it is not discussed in AP 1456.

There is not time to mention all the progress made in air navigation between the wars. Some equipment, such as Directional Gyroscopes by Sperry in America, had a dramatic impact on flying practice[20]. Other equipment, such as the Distant Reading Compass conceived in the late 20's, and equivalent systems invented by Pioneer in America and Pattin in Belgium would not really become important until the production of large bombers[21].

Similarly, directional wireless was available, but there does not seem to have been a standard fit of DF equipment in many aircraft; at least photographs of aircraft taken during this period do not often show DF aerials. One reason, apart from cost, was that Farnborough believed that external DF aerials would create too much drag reducing an aircraft's speed by up to 11 knots. It was not until a Navigation Officer at No 3 Group, Squadron Leader (later Group Captain) N C Ogilvy-Forbes, who had served in Canada and had experience of U.S. equipment, persisted that trials showed the loss of speed to be in the order of 1 knot. It was then decided to fit DF loops to Wellington aircraft[22]. There was, of course, a well developed Signals Branch, who could provide bearings to aircraft from ground stations, but this system, which had been in existence since the First World War had its own limitations.

Much of the progress made during these years was purely as a result of navigation enthusiasts around the world, many of whom had commercial interests. One result of the openness of air navigation development was that the RAF cannot be criticised for being less well prepared than their allies or, indeed, their future enemies. It also should be emphasised that all air forces shared navigation problems and had their share of navigational blunders. Tactical navigation in combat conditions was not an easy problem to consider, and so, in general, it was ignored. At senior levels RAF interest in navigation was extremely limited, and there were many other pressing problems to occupy the air staffs[23]. However, from about 1935, when expansion had begun, the problem of air navigation was brought to the attention of the Air Ministry by a series of unrelated events.

NAVIGATION MISHAPS AND DISASTERS

Fortunately, one of these events was merely embarrassing and not tragic. In 1935 Wing Commander Peter Warburton had the misfortune to lose his way in Iraq while Sir Philip Sassoon, the Under Secretary of State for Air, was on an official visit to the Middle East. Since the Under Secretary's aircraft was used in the extensive and successful search, the matter was reported to the Air Council who asked the Wing Commander for his reasons, in writing, as to how he became lost. His frank reply was that he hadn't the foggiest idea about Navigation and that was hardly surprising as it was not taught by the flying schools.

The main fault was judged to lie with the Central Flying School where pilots were taught to fly upside down and do a variety of other things, but not to go from A to B. The Air Council, therefore, promptly arranged for a Navigation Specialist on Flying Boats, Flight Lieutenant (later Air Marshal Sir Edward) Chilton, to be posted to Wittering from Mount Batten (at a weekend's notice) to give the Station Commander and all the CFS instructors a three-month Navigation Course[24].

Wing Commander Jefford shows from his reading of the Air Ministry Navigation Policy Files, that the Air Council were made aware from about 1936, when the first navigation policy file was opened, that RAF navigation was not up to the standards required to sustain their doctrine of Air Power which depended on "the bomber getting through". In that year, Flight Lieutenant David Waghorn, brother of the well known Schneider Trophy pilot and a recent graduate of the Specialist Navigation Course, wrote a paper criticising the state of navigation in the RAF. This paper was vigorously supported by Group Captain Arthur Harris. The ultimate chain of staff action led to the creation of the Air Navigator trade as we now know it.

Examples of poor navigation, however, were often attributed to "pilot error" and staff action could be slow. It was only with major disasters that the need for better navigation training and equipment was emphasised. One well publicised disaster occurred during the annual Air Defence of Great Britain exercise when a sudden and unexpected change of wind led to many aircraft crews who were relying on the forecast becoming lost. Photographs of one bomber crew being rescued by a trawler were published in newspapers.

Another classic navigational disaster occurred in bad weather in December 1936. Only one of seven Heyford bombers, which set out from Aldergrove in Northern Ireland for Finningley in Yorkshire, navigated safely to its destination. Four of the aircraft crashed, killing three crew and injuring several others. The other two aircraft got away with forced landings and fairly minor damage. This episode became known as the "Retreat from Aldergrove" and its shock waves spread in all directions. For a start, the C.O. was fired[25].

Poor navigation was investigated by Air Chief Marshal Sir Edgar Ludlow-Hewitt when he was appointed C-in-C, Bomber Command, in September 1937. Two months later he reported to the Air Staff that his Command was "unable to operate except in fair weather". Ludlow-Hewitt made a number of recommendations, the main two being the provision of navigational aids and the introduction of a more realistic aircraft crew policy. He noted that the leading European and American airlines flew in adverse weather and at night. Civil pilots could, by 1937, depend upon navigational aids and homing devices, wireless direction finding and a meteorological and control organisation on the ground. These basic peace-time facilities were not widespread in the RAF, and there were no aids designed to work in war. The fact that, as John Terraine noted, there were 478 forced landings of Bomber Command aircraft in 2 years due to pilots losing their way, shows that problems were widespread and not confined to a few incidents. The Bomber Command Efficiency Reports make depressing reading until one remembers that navigational blunders are a general human failing observed in all the aviation minded nations both then and now.

NAVIGATION TRAINING

Most of the RAF's navigation experts had served on the Flying Boat squadrons. In April 1920 a School of Naval Co-operation and Aerial Navigation had been established at Calshot to train pilots posted to Flying Boats. Until 1936 this School, under various names provided the only advanced post-graduate navigation instruction in the RAF on the Long Navigation Course which began in November 1920 on an impromptu basis. This year-long course did not have many students at first, but graduates, such as David Waghorn, Philip Mackworth, Edward Chilton and Kelly Barnes, were to have a great influence on the development of Air Navigation. In addition D C T Bennett, who was to become an Air Vice-Marshal and the commander of the "Pathfinder" force in Bomber Command, became an instructor on the flying boat course at Calshot in the early 30s.

Bennett, whilst at Calshot, had his mind set on a civil aviation career and studied for the civilian navigation licences which were needed for his plans. In contrast, the students at Calshot were generally specialising in navigation in order to remain as permanently commissioned RAF officers. For a few of these students there is the suspicion that this was their sole interest, navigation being a better choice for them than engineering or some other arduous or less interesting specialisation. On the whole, the specialist navigators became dedicated professionals, but their profession suffered continuous losses as promotion and general career postings took navigators away from navigation duties. This point was, indeed, the nub of Waghorn's 1936 paper; there were far too few navigators[26].

Apart from the School at Calshot, the only navigation training was either received during flying training during lessons usually scheduled immediately after lunch or, if an appropriate enthusiast could be found to teach, obtained on the squadron. After one particular financial crisis, it was decided to devolve most training down to Squadron level in order to reduce manning levels, but this measure was not successful. Even before the navigational disasters and the expansion of the RAF an attempt was made to improve matters. In 1932 a practical navigation course for pilots was run at Andover using local resources and in 1933 it was decided to reform the Air Pilotage school which had effectively ceased to exist on completion of its first course at the end of 1919. In 1936 this school and the school at Calshot were both moved to Manston and combined to form the School of Air Navigation. The new school offered, in addition to advanced training, a six-month Navigation Course for pilots proceeding to Coastal Command or staff jobs at group or command headquarters and a three-month Short Navigation Course adapted for those pilots proceeding to Bomber Command. When war began to loom, fortnight-long "crammer" courses were held to indoctrinate Bomber Command squadron and flight commanders in the mysteries of astro.

It must be emphasised again that the students at Manston were pilots and the more realistic aircraft crew policy took some time to mature. The aircrew category of Air Observer, discontinued after

1918, was re-introduced in October 1937. In December 1937 it was decided that the Observer should not be a squadron ground tradesman employed part-time in the air, but should be a full-time professional, trained to assist the pilot with navigation and additionally qualified in bombing and gunnery. There was to be some debate on the role of the observer as navigator which was concluded with the decision that the observer should be responsible for aircraft navigation in peace and war. It was argued, in vain, that only the Captain of the aircraft could be responsible for navigation (and there was certainly no thought, at this stage, that the Observer, as navigator, could or should be the Captain).

A shortage of suitable instructors and suitable aircraft delayed the implementation of this decision. Retired Royal Navy and Merchant Navy officers recruited as instructors had no experience of Air Navigation and their teaching was predictably ill suited to the air navigation task. This might not have been a problem if there had been enough time and flying for students to develop navigation skills at their own pace. After all, Brown, on the Atlantic crossing, had run up his dead reckoning effectively enough using Traverse Tables in the marine manner as well as using modern graphical fixing methods. There was no time for leisurely training in 1939 and less than 50 hours flying was all the trainee observer could expect. Nevertheless, there was a rapid expansion in the number of Air Navigation Schools and some Civil Air Navigation Schools were also established.

RAF NAVIGATION IN 1939

On the face of it, RAF navigation in 1939 was not much different from 1918. Aircraft such as the Anson used for navigation training in 1939, did not have a remarkably improved performance to the aircraft of 1918, but there were significant differences. Enclosed cockpits and standardised instrument panels were increasingly common. Efforts had been made throughout the inter-war years to standardise the RAF blind flying panel, and improvements in small, but significant steps, to all flight instruments had been made. In particular, every observer could expect to fly on an aircraft equipped with a decent aperiodic compass, such as the P6 Type compass. There was also a widespread fit of various types of Drift Sights. Without such instruments, dead reckoning would have remained a very imprecise art. It should be noted in passing that Air Speed Indicators could be calibrated in statute miles per hour or nautical miles per hour depending on aircraft manufacturer or on aircraft role.

More important, the infrastructure to support navigation had been freed from the constraints of the "economy drive" and many small but significant improvements were introduced. For example, a Royal Engineer officer and a small staff from the Geographical Section, General Staff (MI4) at the war office had been responsible for producing specialised small scale maps for visual navigation from about 1934. In about 1938 this Air Ministry Map Branch became the Assistant Directorate of Maps, Air Ministry, and under Lieutenant Colonel J C T Willis (the brother of "AA" of Tee Emm fame) effectively expanded the scope of the section's work. There had also been considerable international activity and agreement on specifications for air maps, such that the airman of 1939 had, in general, no need to rely on RAC road maps or the equivalent overseas product. These maps were produced in addition to the Air Pilots and Route Books (the equivalent to our modern en-route charts) which were widely available[27]. Another example of an improved service was the meteorology service which disseminated hourly reports from all over Europe and around the world. Although the RAF of 1918 did have a well developed support organisation, the contrast between 1918 and 1939 is evident from reading books and magazines from the period. The striking difference is partly explained by the existence of widespread civil and commercial flying but also, by 1939, the RAF was playing a vigorous role. The Station Navigation Officer was becoming more widespread and the Duty Pilot's Rooms better furnished with information by 1939[28].

Navigation could still be a hit-or-miss affair. Given the sudden expansion of the training programme it was not surprising that a consistent air navigation technique was not taught in an entirely standardised way. The translation of AP 1234 into an effective training manual (as opposed to a text book for graduates) was not achieved until 1941. Discussions with the few observers and aircrew who survived on torpedo bomber squadrons reveals that most navigation relied on DR. The technique invariably used seems to have depended on obtaining a drift shortly after departure and then applying this drift to follow a track which aimed to cross a significant line feature, such as the coast, which could be used to lead in to a visual fix point. Most crews would deliberately aim off to one side of a planned fix point and might, with a bit of luck update the drift or obtain a radio bearing from a ground station to boost their confidence. There is no false modesty in these accounts; most observers and pilot navigators readily admit that they didn't have the instruments, facilities or need to practice more sophisticated techniques.

Even with the best technique, there could be problems. An article by Flight Lieutenant Edwin Shipley, a specialist navigator serving in the RAF entitled "Drift Sights, Drift Markings and Ground-Speed Meters" reminds the reader about the importance of obtaining accurate wind information by recounting a problem with obtaining a wind by the "two-fix" or "two-drift" method. A flying boat venturing out into the North Sea from Orfordness needed to find the wind speed in order to obtain an estimate groundspeed for a radius of action type calculation. Unfortunately, the stop watch failed during the procedure and, even more unfortunately, the failure was not noticed until the after flight post-mortem. This failure resulted in the finding of a much reduced wind speed and an embarrassing, although not serious, return to base half an hour overdue. Flight Lieutenant Shipley also included, in an article entitled "Navigation on Long Flights Over the Sea" the following stricture:

> "Of course, there is one way of making a sea crossing – that is to set a precomputed course on leaving the land and to carry straight on until a landfall is made. That is not navigation and sooner or later it will lead one astray – as many have found to their cost![29]"

Flight Lieutenant Shipley was writing for crews who included a dedicated navigator. It must be remembered that the RAF operated many single seat aircraft. Navigation was just as important for these aircraft. The standard practice for fighter pilots was to learn every conceivable landmark in their sector. These aircraft were not expected to navigate long distances. However, the interception of enemy aircraft is a sophisticated navigational problem and the development of radar was one of the most important pointers to the future of navigation. The procedures and electronics involved are well known, but what is less well publicised is that the team that created radar also spawned Operational Research in the RAF[30]. As Slessor was later to admit the achievements of OR were to revolutionise navigation and operational effectiveness in the years after 1939. However, in 1939, only Fighter Command and Dowding enjoyed a close relationship with the scientific and intellectual establishment. The committee which initiated the radar research programme had been established in 1934 on the suggestion of Wimperis. A similar committee founded in 1936 to examine problems of air offence was a failure perhaps because, as Professor Jones maintains, Bomber Command were too complacent[31]. Wimperis and Farnborough had also begun work on ideas which were to result in the Air Position Indicator and the complex navigation systems with which we are familiar today. Many developments would be accelerated by the impetus of the War and by technical co-operation with the United States, but the British intellectual resources had, by 1939, finally been assembled and begun to work on Wimperis's most important unsolved problem, navigation.

CONCLUSION

As Alice said in Wonderland:

"Yes, that's about the right distance – but then I wonder what latitude or longitude I've got to?"

There were four criticisms raised by the post war navigators and historians: navigation technique had remained static; instruments did not receive enough attention; training was spasmodic and ineffective; and, finally, there was a general policy of "laissez faire" or of complacency. This paper has not, so far, set out to directly refute these charges. Now, in conclusion, they will be addressed in turn in order to explicitly discuss the question set by David Page, "what went wrong?"

Beginning with technique it can be argued that, far from remaining static, technique developed in many areas. Admittedly the First World War had seen remarkable developments in navigation so much of the next 21 years saw the consolidation of existing theory, but a comparison of navigation manuals shows that a much deeper understanding of air navigation technique was available by 1939. This particularly applied to astro navigation which was being popularised by the RAF.

With hindsight it might seem that more could have been done to improve instruments, but this view ignores the reality of technical limitations. The overriding problem facing the RAF in this area was the economy drive which restricted investment in establishments such as the RAE. To criticise the RAF for not introducing the Air Positioning Indicator (which itself depended on an effective air mileage unit and the DR compass) is unfair. The technology was simply not ready in 1939. It is worth emphasising once again that because of international co-operation, particularly with the USA, the RAF had access to all the best instruments available to air navigators in the world. No other nation had any better instruments, although it has to be conceded that the RAF undervalued radio navigation aids.

Training was an area considerably affected by the economy drives. It is difficult to pretend that the RAF training system churned out sufficient navigators but Trenchard's intention was for the peacetime Air Force to form a strong nucleus for wartime expansion. The quality of the navigation specialists cannot be doubted, but they formed a very small nucleus. There is a temptation to speculate on what might have been if the Observer trade had not been discarded at the end of the First World War, but such speculation is probably pointless. Undoubtedly the rapid creation of a distinct navigation profession which began in 1937 was a major achievement for the RAF and I believe that, although the training cannot be compared to that available in the later years of the Second World War, it was much better than could be expected given the resources available. In fact given the rapid expansion of the RAF, I believe to have created a navigation profession at all was a remarkable achievement.

Finally, we must address the charge of complacency and neglect of navigation which has been raised against RAF commanders. This charge is difficult to refute, especially as the first years of the Second World War saw some dreadful operational results. But, as this paper has suggested, the RAF commanders made a determined attempt to improve navigation once the extent of the problem became apparent from 1936. It is clear, however, that they did not appreciate the difficulty of tactical navigation and this lack of understanding is what led Professor Jones and others in the scientific world to believe that Senior RAF Officers were complacent. The fact that navigators, such as Kelly Barnes, Mackworth and Waghorn felt they needed to advocate the cause of navigation so vigorously also suggests that the RAF leadership was out of touch with reality. After all, one of the functions of leadership is to find the way, and the RAF was clearly getting lost.

The real problem, I believe, lies with the over ambitious RAF doctrine and dogma and with Trenchard's spirit and willpower with which the RAF was imbued. The RAF offensive philosophy depended on bombers and navigation was just one of many problems faced by bomber crews in 1939. Liddell Hart appreciated this flaw in Trenchard's RAF when he wrote the following just before the War:

"The need today, in air defence as well as in all other spheres, is to adjust the methods to the means, and to take due account of the reality of present conditions."[32]

Although the RAF doctrine was founded on faith and hope, we should judge it with charity. After all, it could be suggested that money spent on bombers would certainly not have been spent on tanks or frigates if the RAF had weakened its resolve, but on cavalry and battleships. The single minded devotion to the bomber was what kept the RAF going. This is the view of the most perceptive historian of the RAF, Sir Maurice Dean[33].

My conclusion then, is that given the investment, there was not much wrong with navigation in 1939, there was just too much faith placed on its effectiveness. As for the navigation specialists, they were to provide one of the means to undertake the great bomber offensive which kept the spirit of resistance to Hitler alive. The years after 1939 were to see the firm establishment of the RAF navigation profession built on solid foundations. Dickie Richardson would wish me to add: as for the place of Air Navigation, the one-time Cinderella of the RAF, Psalm 118 is apposite:

"The stone that the builders refused, the same is become the head of the corner".

A NOTE ON SOURCES

The apparent lack of official interest in navigation in the RAF between the wars is reflected in the paucity of official records devoted to the practice and training of air navigation in the Service. In 1945 the Air Ministry Training Department produced a paper entitled "Notes on the History of Training" but the Section on Air Navigation elicited much criticism from those qualified to comment and it was discarded with ignomiry. An attempt was made at Manby in 1960 to produce a history of the Specialist Navigation Course[34], and a brief outline history of basic Observer and Navigator training was produced at Finningley in 1972[35]. There are a few official publications on navigation, instruments and related subjects in libraries and at the

Public Record Office but, in general, the main source of information lies in isolated references to navigation in the many memoirs of RAF aircrew which have been published in recent years, in contemporary aviation magazines and on the books, papers and notes of the navigation enthusiasts. The most important of these contemporary sources is perhaps the "History of Air Navigation" written by A. J. Hughes at the end of the Second World War. It is also necessary to note that the general development of air navigation before 1941 has been comprehensively chronicled by Monte Wright, whose work remains the most reliable secondary source on the subject[36].

1   Jones R V (1978) *Most Secret War* Chapter 5. Hamish Hamilton.

2   Sir Charles Webster and Noble Frankland, (1961) *The Strategic Air Offensive Against Germany 1939-1945*, HMSO, includes a full account of D M B Butt's statistical investigation of night bombing operations completed in June and July 1941.

3   Group Captain F C Richardson CBE FRIN DBA BCom, was responsible for the 1941 "Alice in Wonderland" edition of AP1234A, the Manual of Air Navigation, and was Deputy Director (Navigation) at the Air Ministry at the time of the Korean War.

4   HMSO (December 1919) *Permanent Organisation of the Air Force. Note by the Secretary of State for Air on a Scheme Outlined by the Chief of Air Staff.* ("Trenchard's White Paper" includes the following: "Firstly, to make an Air Force worthy of the name, we must create an Air Force spirit . . ." The second point was to reduce accidents needed a highly technical service and the third point was that if the Air Force officer was not to be a chauffeur and nothing more than navigation, meteorology, photography and wireless were necessities.)

5   The most substantial work is: Montgomery Hyde, H (1976) *British Air Policy Between the Wars 1918-1939* William Heinemann Ltd. (Montgomery Hyde's vast and comprehensive work ignores RAF navigation completely which is an indication on how little RAF navigation policy there was.)

6   In "The Fight at Odds", the first volume of the Official History of the RAF between 1939 and 1945, Denis Richards.

7   Terraine J (1985) *The Right of the Line.* Hodder and Stoughton Ltd.

8   Hastings, M (1979) *Bomber Command.* Michael Joseph Ltd.

9   Sir Maurice Dean (1979) *The Royal Air Force and Two World Wars.* Cassell Ltd. (Sir Maurice Dean specifically discusses problems with navigation and bombing on page 68. His conclusions on the general problems facing the RAF apply equally to navigation.)

10   Montgomery Hyde, H Opus cited Chapter VI page 277.

11   Barnett C (1986) *The Audit of War.* Macmillan Ltd

12   A copy of the précis was given to me by Group Captain F C Richardson.

13   PRO (1918) AIR 10/316/293 *Instructions for the use of Bigsworth Protractor Parallels and Chart Board.*

14 H E Wimperis was Director of Scientific Research at the Air Ministry from 1925 to 1937.

15 Wing Commander C G Jefford MBE BA RAF Retd (1996) *The Observer in the British Air Services, 1914-1918.* Draft Paper.

16 Such tables can be found in the PRO under AIR 10/2118/1539A, B & C

17 Wing Commander Roderick Hill: "The Baghdad Air Mail"

18 Weems P V H (1931) *Air Navigation.* McGraw Hill (This work ran to several editions including a British Empire Edition. It was one of the best navigation text books of its day.)

19 Hughes A J (1946) *The History of Air Navigation.* George Allen and Unwin Ltd. (Hughes had an interest in publicising his company, a noted manufacturer of navigation instruments, and was a key figure in the development of air navigation; his history is a prime, if sometimes narrowly focussed and rambling, source.)

20 Williams J E D (1944) *From Sails to Satellites.* Oxford University Press. (This work is an authoritative source on navigation history which discusses the more important navigational developments in this period.)

21 Hughes *Opus* Cited, page 111, credits Captain L C Bygrave and P A Cooke with the invention of the DR Compass in 1926. Twiney F J et al (1946) *Development of Automatic Dead Reckoning Navigation 1939-1945.* (RAE Report No IAP 1462) gives the sole credit for the DR compass to Bygrave and gives the following dates; 1931 start of development work, 1935 first service trials, 1938 first contract and 1941 fitting to Stirling aircraft. The DR compass did not become a practical proposition until an ac transmission system was devised and aircraft became large enough to carry it. The Pattin system was adopted by the Luftwaffe.

22 This account is taken from Group Captain Richardson's notes of a conversation with Air Marshal Sir Edward Chilton on 2 June 1988.

23 Sir John Slessor (1956) *The Central Blue.* Cassell & Co. Ltd. (This book gives a good impression of the confusion and chaos in British defence planning before the War.)

24 Air Marshal Sir Edward Chilton in conversation on 2 June 1988.

25 Air Marshal Sir Edward Chilton in conversation on 2 June 1988.

26 Group Captain Richardson calculated that as late as 1932 there were only 14 qualified navigation specialists in the RAF at senior officer level.

27 Several Route Books survive in the PRO, for example AIR 10/2116/1536/1, Plymouth to Basra (1931) and AIR 10/2116/1536/2 Calcutta to Singapore (1931).

28 Group Captain Richardson was very critical of flight planning facilities and of the reliability of meteorological forecasts, particularly overseas. But I believe that there was a marked improvement, at least at home, by 1939.

29 Articles in Volume III of *Newnes Aeronautics.* (1939) George Newnes Ltd., London. (There are a number of articles on navigation in this work written by specialist navigation officers from the School of Navigation.)

30 AP 3368 *The Origins and Development of Operational Research in the Royal Air Force* (1963) HMSO, London pages xvii to xx.

31 Jones R V *Opus Cited* page 67.

32 Liddell Hart (1939) *The Defence of Britain* (quoted by Montgomery Hyde).

33 Dean *Opus Cited* pages 67-69 and Chapter 21.

34 This history is being rewritten by Mr P Saxon.

35 Wing Commander Jefford remembers producing this document when he was on the staff as a navigation instructor.

36 Wright M D (1972) *Most Probable Position.* The University Press of Kansas.

5. The Epic Flights

Wing Commander "Jeff" Jefford

Chairman's Introduction:

We are now going to turn our attention to the epic flights, and who more qualified than Wing Commander "Jeff" Jefford to talk to us about these flights. "Jeff" spent 32 years in the RAF, flying Canberras and Vulcans as well as a number of instructor and staff appointments. On leaving the RAF in 1991 he went back to school and took a First Class Honours degree in History at London University; and he has two excellent books to his credit . . . "Jeff" . . .

Oddly enough, the rather stirring title of my presentation turns out to be something of a cuckoo in today's navigational nest. Lots of remarkable long range flights were made between the wars, of course, and many of these were epic. But, as we shall see, while they were epic in terms of their duration and the distances covered, the methods of navigation employed were generally pretty pedestrian.

I have a suspicion that, unless we actually think about it, there is a fairly widespread perception that we, the British, probably did more than anyone else to open up the world to aviation. We didn't. Many other nations made major contributions, notably the French, the Dutch, the Italians, the Americans, the Portuguese, the Spanish and the Russians. The same is true of personalities. We British had our heroes, but so did others so that for every Alcock and Brown there was a Coutinho and Cabral; for every Amy Johnson a Ruth Nichols and for every Alan Cobham a Dieudonné Costes. Furthermore, most of these personalities were civilians, the point being that trail-blazing and record-breaking were essentially civilian, rather than military occupations. This is not to say that the RAF played no part in long-range aviation. It did but, since we are considering today the development of navigation in the Royal Air Force, I shall bias a lot of what I have to say to reflect service activities.

The obvious yardstick with which to measure progress in long range flying is the state of the world's record for non-stop great circle distance flown. This was broken fourteen times between 1925, when it was first officially recognised, and 1938. The UK had held it only once, however, so it is clear that a lot of other people must have been quite keen on long-distance flying. Why? There were three imperatives driving long-distance aviation – **Commerce** (which includes winning prizes), **Empire** and **Prestige**. Some combination of these three factors lay behind every significant long-range flight undertaken between the wars.

Surprisingly however, navigation wasn't at the top of the list of priorities of early long-distance aviators – I'd guess that it came about fourth. The three most pressing questions that a trail-blazer had to ask himself – for each of perhaps twenty stages – were:

1   Will the engine keep going long enough to get me to my next destination?
2   Will there be somewhere sensible to land *if* I get there?
3   Will Shell be there to refuel me?

South of the Black Sea and the Mediterranean the normal means of transport involved camels, horses, elephants and the like. They did not run on petrol, of course, so there wasn't a lot of it about. As a result, refuelling presented quite a problem 'down route' in the 1920s, the point being that there was no 'route'. The big oil companies were international organisations, of course, and petrol could be made available anywhere – so long as the long-distance flyer had made the necessary arrangements in advance.

My first three questions can be boiled down to **Reliability, Planning** and **Logistics.** Only after one had attended to these crucial factors was it necessary to ask:

4   How will I get from A to B, from B to C, and so on?

The answer to this one was almost invariably by air pilotage, a combination of rule-of-thumb dead reckoning and map-reading – what we would call 'pilot nav'.

Having, I hope, sharpened the perspective a little, I will enlarge on my three basic reasons behind long-distance flying and then have a look at just a few examples. If Commerce, Empire and Prestige were the reasons why everyone did it, how did these relate specifically to the RAF? Nine answers to this question are offered at Figure 1. They are in no particular order of importance and the items are not mutually exclusive – any particular expedition might well have reflected half-a-dozen of these.

Seriously long-distance flying began as early as 1917 when, as an exercise in **Power Projection,** Sqn Cdr Kenneth Savory flew an

LONG RANGE DRIVERS (FOR THE RAF)

Power Projection	'Staff College speak' for dropping (or threatening to drop) bombs on people who lived a *long* way away.
Imperial Communications	The establishment and maintenance of an imperial route network was vital to the UK's interests in the 1920s and 1930s
Deployment	....of units to new bases under their own steam.
Defence Sales	...to sustain an aircraft industry starved of RAF orders.
Prestige	Propaganda for consumption abroad, to maintain and/or enhance Britain's reputation in an era of increasingly militant nationalism on the Continent and elsewhere.
Publicity	Propaganda for consumption at home, to keep the air force in the public eye (and to encourage politicians to favour the RAF Vote?).
Showing the Flag	Much cheaper than 'sending a gunboat' and particularly useful in the context of colonial peacekeeping.
Reinforcement	Mutual support between adjacent overseas Commands in times of tension, particularly from mid-1930s.
Training	Long-range, multi-stage exercises, fostered captaincy and self-reliance.

Figure 1

RNAS Handley Page from Manston to Mudros in the Aegean – some 2,000 miles in 32 flying hours spread over seventeen days. Savory had done his **Planning** and he took his **Logistics** with him – his aeroplane carried a spare propeller lashed on top of its fuselage and he had almost enough spare parts on board to build a third engine.

Late in 1918 two RAF Handley Pages were flown out to Egypt. The first one was piloted by Maj Archie Maclaren and the colourful Brigadier 'Biffy' Borton with technical support being provided by Sgt Goldfinch and AM Francis. This aeroplane reached Egypt in a flight time of 36 hours – attracting AFCs and AFMs all round.

How did Maclaren and Co. navigate? The weather was very kind and, in essence, they just followed their maps. This is not to say that it was easy, however, especially if you didn't pay attention – Borton's report on their expedition noted that it took the Handley Page $2^3/_4$ hours to fly the 180-mile leg from Pisa to Rome while an Italian pilot doing the same trip in a Caproni managed to lose his bearings and did not turn up for seven hours! Nevertheless, (careful) map-reading sufficed and Borton states that they never had to resort to using their Campbell-Harrison Course and Distance Calculator *or* their Bigsworth Chartboard and Protractor. Two destroyers were on station for the Mediterranean crossing between Crete and North Africa but they never saw either of them – an undetected change in the wind had caught them out and they eventually coasted-in about forty miles east of their planned landfall and a rather alarming forty minutes late. While navigation had been fairly routine, their success had been heavily dependent upon **Planning** and **Logistics** and the entire route had been pre-stocked, with POL at every stop and spare wheels, tyres, propellers and the like at strategic intervals.

The second Handley Page to reach Egypt was subsequently used to make the first ever flight to India, thus making a major contribution to another of my list of drivers – **Imperial Communications.** Piloted by Capt Ross Smith and Brigadier Borton and with Maj Gen Geoffrey Salmond on board, the aeroplane left Cairo late in 1918. After a reasonably trouble-free passage, via Damascus, Baghdad, the Persian Gulf and Delhi, it eventually got as far east as Calcutta. This trip was particularly influential and I shall mention it again.

Moving on, to another of my long-distance imperatives, let us consider an early **Deployment.** With the war over, it was decided to move three full squadrons of heavy bombers from France to Egypt.

Encouraged by the success of the three wartime flights to the Near East, the aeroplanes were to be flown out, beginning in May 1919. This turned out to be less straightforward than had been hoped. Of the fifty-one Handley Pages which set out, nineteen were wrecked, representing an accident rate of something like 85 flying hours per cat 5. The losses were not *all* due to flying accidents but many were and eight men lost their lives. The RAF learned a great deal about the importance of **Reliability** from this first attempt at *sustained* long-distance flying and we didn't try it again for nearly ten years.

The first of many flights undertaken by the RAF with the specific aim of promoting **Defence Sales** was a 2,500 mile Scandinavian tour made by a Felixstowe F.5 in the summer of 1919. Two aircraft should have made this trip but one was obliged to drop out at Dundee on the outbound leg. Navigation was done by making the shortest possible crossing of the North Sea and coast crawling the rest of the way. We didn't sell any flying-boats incidentally – not to the Scandinavians anyway.

While Maj Christopher Galpin's flying-boat had been feeling its way around the Skagerrak, the rigid airship R 34 was making a *real* pioneering flight, the first east-west crossing of the Atlantic and the first double crossing. The main driver this time was **Prestige,** in the hopes of promoting **Sales.** Commanded by Maj George Scott, the ship flew to Long Island and back during July 1919. Flight times were $4^{1}/_{2}$ days outbound and 3 days for the return leg, averaging ground-speeds of 35 and 48mph.

How did the R 34 find its way? By dead reckoning, at about 2,000 feet. Drift could be established by observation of a sea marker as it was left astern and groundspeed was measured by timing the passage of the ship's shadow, which was some 700 feet long, as it passed over an object in the sea. With heading and airspeed already known it was possible to calculate the wind velocity. Since most airship men were ex-RNAS, and many had been sailors before that, they were also quite good at estimating the *surface* wind by the observation of wind lanes.

Fixing was another matter. A few radio bearings were obtained at the beginning and end of each voyage and the ship also carried on-board D/F equipment, although it was found that ground trans-missions were too brief for useful bearings to be obtained. Astro was used but with indifferent results. On the outbound journey, for instance, only three of the seventeen observations taken had the advantage of a sea horizon; the others had to make do with a cloud horizon which rendered them of doubtful accuracy. Even when a clear horizon could be used there were still problems with accuracy as it was necessary to know the airship's height above the surface in order to allow for the error arising from using a depressed datum, rather than the true horizontal. Their altimeters were not much help because they had no idea of the surface pressure in mid-Atlantic and they were understandably disinclined to take their huge and cumbersome craft down to sea level in order to measure it. The ship's navigation officer, Maj Gilbert Cooke, eventually solved the problem by using a sextant to measure the angle subtended by the craft's shadow on the sea – this was of known length and, by using trigonometry, it was possible to calculate the ship's altitude. At one stage Cooke reckoned that the altimeters were some 900 feet in error. A pressure reading obtained by wireless from a ship estimated to be about sixty miles away indicated an error of 1,000 feet. Since the difference could be accounted for by the sixty miles separation, Cooke's calculations were accepted without question thereafter. He later estimated that in mid-Atlantic he had probably known the whereabouts of the airship within 50 miles, which was good enough – after all, they were hardly likely to bump into anyone else over the Atlantic in 1919.

Although I said that I would be concentrating on RAF activities, while we are dealing with **Prestige** (and **Publicity**) I really cannot ignore the three £10,000 prizes which were on offer in 1919 for the first Transatlantic flight, the first UK-Australia flight (by an Australian) and the first flight from Cairo to the Cape of Good Hope – a £10,000 purse would probably be worth something like £200,000 today.

The Americans actually claimed the title of being 'first across' the Atlantic in May 1919 when the U.S. Navy did it in stages via the Azores and Portugal. No fewer than sixty naval vessels were stationed at roughly fifty mile intervals along the entire route to provide wireless relay facilities and navigational markers. In the awful weather many of them were never sighted and only one of the three Curtiss flying-boats involved actually completed the trip.

About a dozen teams, all of them privately-sponsored, registered for the main event, the *Daily Mail's* Atlantic 'race'. Only four reached the start line. Three actually had a go. The only successful crew were

Alcock and Brown who made it on 14/15th June. How did they navigate? In short, with great difficulty. Arthur Brown used a Baker Navigation Machine to help with astro but, with the weather against them, they managed only one Sun shot, which provided a ground-speed check after about $4^1/_2$ hours, and a Vega/Polaris fix four hours later. Flying on through rain and sleet, it was four hours after dawn before Brown was able to get another sight of the Sun – that is, seven hours since their last fix. Forty minutes later he was able to see the sea and measure his drift. Hand-written notes from Brown to the pilot such as "Keep her nearer 120 than 140" provide some idea of the precision with which it was possible to maintain the desired heading and an indication of the accuracy with which they actually *knew* their whereabouts is suggested by one of the final entries in Brown's log which noted "Crossed land at 8.25 on the 15th. Probably northern Ireland."

Since the Atlantic crossing was *the* great aviation challenge at the time, one wonders why the British Government, that is the RAF, did not compete. One answer is that we probably couldn't afford to! On deeper reflection, however, it can be seen that the Atlantic was of little *strategic* significance. The only things on the other side were Canadians and Americans and whatever else they were they weren't a threat. The RAF had quite enough on its plate in the other direction where the newly-acquired Middle Eastern empire had to be pacified and defended, where the Indian frontier was unstable, and where there was a pressing need to improve communications with the relatively isolated South Africans, Australians and New Zealanders. In this imperial context the Atlantic was of little consequence and it is interesting, but still perhaps a little surprising, to observe that, apart from the R 34, no RAF aeroplane ever flew the Atlantic in either direction until well after the establishment of ATFERO in WW II – and that was set up using civilian, rather than military, expertise.

Moving on to the Australia flight, the winners were the Smith brothers with Sgts Bennett and Shires in another Vimy. They started out on 12th November 1919 and landed at Darwin twenty-nine days later. Six other teams had a go. All of them experienced severe problems. Three aeroplanes crashed catastrophically, with the loss of four lives. One crew was arrested in Yugoslavia where they were jailed as spies. Another had to resort to using hand grenades to defend themselves from marauding Baluchis. Only one other crew made it to

Australia, Parer and McIntosh in a DH 9 – they crashed four times *en route* and it took them seven months. I think that the overall picture that this conveys underlines my theme – the priorities were **Reliability, Planning** and **Logistics** and the greatest of these was **Reliability.**

For the flight to Australia, none of the competitors did anything very clever in the way of navigation – it was essentially a map-reading exercise. The most difficult stage was the seven-hour crossing of the Timor Sea and to provide the Smiths with a track check the Australian cruiser *Sydney* was stationed half-way across – more advanced **Planning** you see. In fact **Planning** had been crucial to the Smith's success. When 'Biffy' Borton and Ross Smith had made their pioneering flight from Egypt to India at the end of 1918 they had gone on to assess the feasibility of a flight to Australia by travelling all the way to Koepang by sea. This exploratory expedition had proved to be an adventure in itself as their first ship exploded and sank beneath them!

The success of that first flight to India was also significant in the case of the third major prize, as it had stimulated a great deal of early optimism over the prospects for setting up imperial air routes to the east and to South Africa. In pursuit of the latter goal Salmond had dispatched survey parties to prepare a route to the Cape. By the end of 1919 this task was complete, some forty-three potential LGs had been identified and a comprehensive brief on the route was prepared for the competitors. Presented in an easily assimilated diagrammatic format, the information it contained included: the name, elevation, and co-ordinates of each LG, and the distances between them; the total distance run from Cairo at each LG; the alternative form of transport at each stage, e.g. river steamer, trekking and, further south, railways; the quantity of POL which had been stockpiled at each LG (as at January 1920); the availability of telegraph or telephone communications; and details of the locations, operating authorities and frequencies of the radio stations to work. This amounted to what we might call an En Route Document today – and it was a very good effort for 1920, especially for a route which had yet to be flown. But, once again, it shows the central place of **Planning** in these early endeavours.

Five teams entered the race, four of which had first to fly out from the UK – one life was lost in the process and one aeroplane failed to get as far as Egypt. Four crews had a go – all four fell by the wayside. The eventual 'winners' were a team sponsored by the South African Government, Van Ryneveld, Brand, Newman and Sharratt. They crashed their Vimy near Wadi Halfa whereupon General Smuts made a personal appeal on their behalf and the RAF stumped up a replacement. The crew eventually broke this one taking off from Bulawayo and a DH 9 was flown up to them from Pretoria so that the two pilots, at least, could complete the course by air. Changing aeroplanes had disqualified the crew for the *Daily Mail's* £10,000 prize but, in the event, Smuts managed to rustle up a similar sum from 'petty cash'.

Much of the trip to South Africa had been flown under what were for contemporary aeroplanes, extremely 'hot and high' conditions, which had caused a number of take-off and landing incidents. But navigation had been relatively straightforward – the only really difficult stretch had been crossing the marshlands of the *Sudd* in southern Sudan but otherwise it had been essentially a question of heading south and following the general line of the Nile, the Rift Valley and then railway lines.

There had been a significant imperial interest underpinning two of these three pioneering ventures and I cannot really leave **Imperial Communications** without making some mention of Sir Alan Cobham whose personal contribution to British aviation was second to none. The heyday of Cobham's trail-blazing was in 1924-26 when he made three quite remarkable 'epic' flights, all in the same single-engined DH 50 – London to Rangoon and back; London to Cape Town and back; and London to Melbourne and back – 62,000 miles in all, usually accompanied by his regular engineer, Arthur Elliot. Most long distance flights undertaken prior to this had been made in war surplus bombers but the DH 50 was a relatively 'modern', or at least a post-war, aeroplane. This was reflected in a significant improvement in its **Reliability,** permitting this to slip down the priority list to leave **Planning** at the top. Cobham excelled at this and his long-range flights were masterpieces of organisation. No amount of planning could cater for every circumstance, however, and while he was flying from Baghdad to Basra on the Australia trip a disenchanted Arab took a pot-shot at the aeroplane and hit Elliot, who died shortly after they landed at Shaibah. Shocked, but undeterred, by this tragedy Cobham arranged to borrow Sgt A H Ward from No. 84 Sqn and carried on.

The RAF entered the long-distance flying game in earnest in 1926 when a Cape Flight was set up at Northolt under Wg Cdr Conway Pulford. They were allocated seven Fairey IIIDs, of which four were shipped out to Egypt to attempt the flight. The other three were dismantled and prepositioned as a source of spares in Egypt, Kenya and South Africa along with several additional engines *and* technical support parties – **Planning** and **Logistics.** As it happened the original four aeroplanes kept going all the way to Cape Town and back to Egypt where their wheels were replaced by floats before they all flew back to the UK. The 14,000 mile round trip took four months. As to navigation; all four aeroplanes had P.2 compasses for the pilots and, for taking bearings, two had O.2 compasses mounted in the rear cockpits. So far as method was concerned, they kept it simple; they applied the forecast (often the statistical) wind, steered the resultant heading, tweaked it with drifts and kept track of distance run by reference to the map. Solid – reliable – but not too demanding really.

In 1928 the new base at Singapore was to be provided with its first resident flying unit – an exercise in **Self Deployment.** In the course of this the unit was to carry out an extended cruise to ascertain the feasibility of flying boats operating more or less independently for prolonged periods. With Gp Capt Henry Cave-Brown-Cave in command, the expedition's four Southamptons left Felixstowe in October 1927. With planned lengthy pauses *en route,* it took four months to reach Seletar. After a six-week break to scrape off the barnacles, they set off again, bound this time for Australia. They circumnavigated the entire continent, counter-clockwise, before returning to Singapore. Another short break was followed by a cruise to Hong Kong via Borneo and the Philippines, returning via Indo-China and Siam.

As always, the key to success had been **Planning** and **Logistics.** Portable gear to permit engines and struts to be replaced while afloat had been designed and built and this kit leapfrogged along the route by sea. The unit also had fourteen replacement engines available and spares pack-ups were sent ahead to strategic locations (Karachi, Singapore, Melbourne, Manila and so on). Furthermore, much had changed since the Smith brothers had passed this way in 1919 and, apart from the Royal Australian Air Force, there were now well-established colonial air forces in the Dutch East Indies, the (American) Philippines and French Indo-China, all of which had

provided assistance and hospitality. The wanderings of the RAF's Far
East Flight had certainly been 'epic' in terms of distance flown – a
total of 27,000 miles – but the rapidly developing international infra-
structure of aerodromes, alighting areas, W/T stations and met
facilities meant that the uncertainty of long distance flying was
rapidly disappearing.

How did the flying-boats navigate? The majority of the trip had
been spent hugging a coastline or a major river, or island hopping –
so most of the time they had simply followed their maps. When
something more esoteric was called for they used the tried and tested
method of maintaining track by laying off the observed drift. The trip
report notes that on the 470 miles sea leg between the Philippines and
Hong Kong, which was flown in a 25 knot beam wind, they made
their landfall within 15 miles after $6^{1}/_{2}$ hours – that's about 3% of
distance flown or 2.3 miles per hr – which, in my experience,
compares quite well with GREEN SATIN and a GPI 4A on a long sea
crossing. The report did stress, however, that this sort of performance
could not be expected from operational boats whose compasses had
to cope with the magnetic influence of military gear – particularly
Lewis guns being swung about on Scarff rings. The report also noted
that while the aeroplanes had carried sextants they had not been used
– apart from there having been no need to use them, the crews had
often been unable to obtain time checks of the necessary accuracy.

Moving on to **Training** – once the wartime wooden Bristol
Fighters and Ninaks began to be replaced by all-metal aeroplanes
from about 1927 relatively local navigation exercises began to be
replaced by much longer 'cruises', as they were known, or survey
flights to more remote destinations, both with the aim of **Showing the
Flag.** There are sufficient events listed at Figure 2 to show that by the
early 1930s line squadrons were frequently undertaking 6,000-mile
round trips and sometimes covering much longer distances.

We have already heard something of the development of navigational instruments and techniques between the wars but we should
appreciate that these new toys were largely the playthings of a tiny
group of enthusiasts. The vast majority of the long-range flying
actually being done out there, 'in the field', was done by ordinary
squadron crews using a 1918 pattern Drift Sight, a Bearing Plate of
similar vintage and a map that just might have been surveyed by
Captain Cook or Doctor Livingstone. If they were *really* lucky, of

course, they might also have had the benefit of the advice of a group captain or an air commodore from Command who had invited himself along for the trip – you know, like they do.

With the steady deterioration in international relations during the 1930s, these training 'cruises' began to give way to **Reinforcement** exercises as the British began to face up to the very uncomfortable fact that having acquired the largest empire the world had ever seen – it was, in practical terms, virtually impossible to defend. To circumvent the shortage of aeroplanes a policy of mutual reinforcement between adjacent Commands was adopted. Figure 3 provides an indication of the sort of thing that was being done, usually at full squadron strength. It is worth noting that some of these deployments had overtones of **Power Projection,** cases in point being the deployment of Scapas to Egypt during the Abyssinia crisis of 1935 and the basing of two squadrons of Singapores in Algeria during 1937 to protect British shipping during the Spanish Civil War. The report on the joint 45/216 Sqn trip to South Africa in 1934 had a little to say about navigation – they used 1:2,000,000 topos which they found "inaccurate and misleading" so track-crawling wasn't a good idea and the technique used was described as good old "compass course and drift".

Finally I must return to two of the long-range drives that I have mentioned before. **Prestige** – to impress the rest of the world, and **Publicity** – for home consumption. The World's Long-Distance Record. The RAF made its first bid for the title in 1927 using a heavily overloaded Hawker Horsley with its fuel capacity more than quadrupled to 1,100 gallons. Flt Lts Roderick Carr and Leonard Gillman attempted to fly it to Karachi but they were eventually obliged to ditch in the Persian Gulf. Nevertheless, by covering 3,420 miles they had actually broken the French record which they had set out to beat. Sadly, however, this was no longer good enough. The RAF's thunder had been stolen by Charles Lindbergh who had flown from New York to Paris five days before, moving the goal posts by a couple of hundred miles in the process. After two more unsuccessful attempts with a second Horsley the Air Ministry ordered a purpose-built aircraft – the Fairey Long-Range Monoplane. In April 1929 Sqn Ldr Arthur Jones-Williams and Flt Lt Norman Jenkins tried to fly it to Bangalore but adverse headwinds made it prudent to land at Drigh Road – a very respectable 4,130 miles, but not far enough to beat the

EXAMPLES OF RAF LONG-RANGE CRUISES 1925-34

Year	Unit	Type	From	To	Senior Pilot (Detachment Commander)
1925	47 Sqn	3 × DH 9A	Cairo	Nigeria	Sqn Ldr A Coningham
1926	216 Sqn	2 × Victoria	Cairo	Aden	Wg Cdr L D D McKean (Air Cdre C R Samson)
1927	47 Sqn	4 × Fairey IIIF	Cairo	Cape Town	Sqn Ldr C R Maxwell (Air Cdre C R Samson)
1927	Comp Flt	3 × Fairey IIIF	Cairo	Nigeria	Wg Cdr F W Stent
1927/28	FE Flt	4 × Southampton	UK	S'pore-Oz-Pl-HK	Gp Capt H M Cave-Brown-Cave
1928	47 Sqn	5 × Fairey IIIF	Cairo	Cape Town	Flt Lt O R Gayford (AVM T I Webb-Bowen)
1929	47 Sqn	4 × Fairey IIIF	Khartoum	Cape Town	Sqn Ldr C R Cox
1929	45 Sqn	3 × Fairey IIIF	Cairo	Nigeria	Sqn Ldr F J Vincent
1930	14 Sqn	4 × Fairey IIIF	Cairo	Cape Town	Sqn Ldr C B Greet
1930	209 Sqn	2 × Iris	UK	Iceland	Wg Cdr S Smith
1930	201 Sqn	4 × Southampton	UK	Baltic cruise	Sqn Ldr E F Turner (Gp Capt E R C Nanson)
1930	47 Sqn	3 × Fairey IIIF	Port Sudan	Gambia	Sqn Ldr E L Howard-Williams
1931	216 Sqn	3 × Victoria	Cairo	Cape Town	Sqn Ldr H W G J Penderel (Gp Capt E M Murray)
1931	202 Sqn	6 × Fairey IIIF (FP)	Malta	Med cruise	Wg Cdr F G D Hards
1931	209 Sqn	2 × Iris	UK	Egypt	Sqn Ldr J H O Jones
1931	45 Sqn	4 × Fairey IIIF	Helwan	Nigeria	Sqn Ldr F J Vincent (Air Cdre R P Ross)
1931/32	205 Sqn	3 × Southampton	Singapore	Andamans	Wg Cdr A C Wright
1932	14 Sqn	4 × Fairey IIIF	Cairo	East Africa	Flt Lt R L R Atcherley (Wg Cdr A T Harris)

1932	8 Sqn	4 × Fairey IIIF	Aden	Cairo	Sqn Ldr R S Sorley
1932	216 Sqn	3 × Victoria	Cairo	Somaliland	Wg Cdr E A B Rice
1932	202 Sqn	4 × Fairey IIIF	Malta	Khartoum	Sqn Ldr H W Evens
1932	205 Sqn	3 × Southampton	Singapore	Australia	Wg Cdr A C Wright
1932	210 Sqn	3 × Southampton	UK	Baltic cruise	Wg Cdr R Leckie
1933	28 Sqn	4 × Wapiti	NW India	Singapore	Flt Lt V E Groom
1933	36 Sqn	4 × Horsley	Singapore	NW India	Sqn Ldr T A Langford-Sainsbury
1933	6 Sqn	5 × Gordon	Cairo	Nyasaland	Flt Lt F R D Swain (Gp Capt C W H Pulford)
1933	205 Sqn	3 × Southampton	Singapore	Borneo	Sqn Ldr E J P Burling (Gp Capt A H Jackson)
1933	202 Sqn	5 x Fairey IIIF (FP)	Malta	Adriatic/Aegean	Sqn Ldr A H Wann
1933	204 Sqn	4 × Southampton	UK	Baltic cruise	Sqn Ldr K B Lloyd
1933	216 Sqn	3 × Victoria	Cairo	West Africa	Sqn Ldr E G Hilton
1933	55 Sqn	4 × Wapiti	Iraq	NW India	Flt Lt H J Gammel
1933	203 Sqn	2 × Rangoon	Iraq	Aden	Gp Capt R E Saul (Air Cdre A D Cunningham)
1934	84 & 70 Sqns	4 × Wapiti & 2 × Victoria	Iraq	Singapore	Sqn Ldr S F Vincent/Flt Lt P V Williams
1934	205 Sqn	3 × Southampton	Singapore	HK via PI	Sqn Ldr K B Lloyd (Gp Capt S W Smith)
1934	202 Sqn	5 x Fairey IIIF (FP)	Malta	Khartoum	Wg Cdr J H O Jones
1934	203 Sqn	3 x Rangoon	Iraq	Australia	Gp Capt R E Saul

Figure 2

EXAMPLES OF INTER-THEATRE AIR REINFORCEMENT EXERCISES

Year	Unit	Type	From	To
1934	No 45 Sqn	Fairey IIIF	Egypt	Iraq
1934	No 45 Sqn	Fairey IIIF	Egypt	South Africa
1934	No 216 Sqn	Victoria	Egypt	South Africa
1935	No 39 Sqn	Hart	India	Singapore
1935	No 204 Sqn	Scapa	UK	Egypt
1937	No 209 Sqn	Singapore	UK	Algeria
1937	No 210 Sqn	Singapore	UK	Algeria
1937	No 11 Sqn	Hart	India	Singapore
1937	No 27 Sqn	Wapiti	India	Singapore
1937	No 70 Sqn	Valentia	Iraq	Singapore
1937	No 84 Sqn	Vincent	Iraq	Singapore
1937	No 203 Sqn	Singapore	Iraq	Singapore
1937	No 45 Sqn	Vincent	Egypt	India
1938	No 39 Sqn	Hart	India	Singapore
1938	No 60 Sqn	Wapiti	India	Singapore
1938	No 70 Sqn	Valentia	Iraq	Singapore
1938	No 84 Sqn	Vincent	Iraq	Singapore
1938	No 203 Sqn	Singapore	Iraq	Singapore

Figure 3

record, which was now held by the Italians. The same crew tried again in December, aiming for Walvis Bay in South West Africa. The aeroplane hit a mountain in Tunisia, probably due to altimeter error, and both crew members were killed.

The Ministry ordered a second Fairey, this one having a number of improvements, including an autopilot. Crewed by Sqn Ldr Oswald Gayford and Flt Lt Gilbert Nicholetts the aeroplane headed south on 6th February 1933. Navigating by drifts and pinpoints until they were over the Sahara in darkness, Nicholetts used astro to fix their position at about midnight. After dawn haze and dust made fixing difficult but their confidence was restored by a positive identification of Fernando Po. Bad weather made the second night much more difficult with the autopilot packing up shortly after daybreak while they were flying in cloud. No longer sure of their whereabouts, they turned west to pick up the coast which they then followed. They finally landed at Walvis Bay after more than 57 hours in the air. They had set a new record for Great Circle distance flown – 5,309 miles. Since the UK already held the absolute records for both speed and altitude, in terms of **Prestige,** this was a most impressive British hat trick.

By 1937 the record was held by the Soviet Union and the RAF was preparing to have another go. Commanded by Wg Cdr Gayford the Long Range Development Unit was established at Upper Heyford with five crews and eight Wellesley bombers, five of which were extensively modified. After a lengthy work-up, during which one aeroplane and its crew were lost, the unit deployed to Egypt, its ultimate destination being Darwin.

The three aircraft which made the record attempt took off on 5th November 1938, each crew flying independently at about 10,000 feet. Four ships were stationed along the route and radio contact was made with each of these, although cloud precluded their actually being sighted. Navigation was by DR and drift, monitored by visual fixes, D/F bearings from ground stations and astro – particularly during the night overflight of India. Over the Bay of Bengal they ran into heavy thunderstorms which they tried to fly around but this complicated dead reckoning and in the end they just let the autopilots fly them through the weather, although they did catch a reassuring glimpse of the Andamans. The second night was spent crossing the East Indies and again, much of this time was spent in heavy cloud and rain, precluding much use of astro. Conditions improved after dawn, permitting position to be fixed by map reading. Hogan's aircraft had a marginal fuel state and he made a precautionary landing at Koepang. Even so their flight was duly ratified as a world record. It was immediately eclipsed, of course, by that of the other two crews, who were jointly credited with 7,158 miles.

So there you have it gentlemen. A *very* rapid canter through the 'epic' flights of the inter-war era – a *little* of what was done, *why* it was done and *how* it was done. What did it teach us? Lessons that are still valid today – that mechanical **Reliability** is essential, that it helps to be lucky but that the need for luck can be minimised by thorough **Planning** backed up by sound **Logistics.**

What did it *not* teach us? Sadly, how to navigate. In essence the methods used by the RAF throughout the inter-war years had been well-understood in 1917. There was one significant innovation that hasn't been mentioned, however – the proliferation of Route Books. The first of these was published in 1922. It amounted to a strip map, showing in considerable detail, all 850 miles of the Cairo-Baghdad Air Mail link. In 1931 a set of such documents was introduced, as the AP 1540 series, to cover the entire UK-Singapore imperial trunk route and from 1937 onwards a whole raft of them began to appear dealing with other links, like Aden to Karachi and Port Sudan to Kano – all of them addressed the differing requirements of landplanes and seaplanes. These Route Books represented the ultimate in 'Bradshawing' but, as Arthur Harris pointed out in 1936 – that's Gp Capt Arthur Harris, DDPlans, 'Bradshawing' wasn't the answer *to* navigation, it was actually a substitute *for* it! What was needed, he said, was experience of using astro and radio direction finding; but we weren't doing that in 1936.

Before closing I have one last word to say about **Reliability.** While industry provided the RAF with equipment of ever improving quality, it was only kept working through the efforts of our ground-crew. Sound maintenance was (and is) as crucial to success as skilled piloting and navigating – many of you will have heard of Henry Cave-Brown-Cave, Oswald Gayford, Gerry Livock, Pulford, Kellett, Burnett and the rest – but who knows the names of *any* inter-war 'erks'?

My final slide shows Sqn Ldr Kellett's Wellesley being worked on at Ismailia. I would draw your attention to the chap on the ladder on the right – the one working on the engine. He joined the RAF at the aged of sixteen as a Halton apprentice in 1929 – the 20th Entry. By this time he was an LAC Fitter One – he got his corporal out of this effort. He eventually retired as a squadron leader engineer in 1968. That, gentlemen, is my Dad, that is!

Note: It was necessary to edit my lecture to stay within the allotted 30 minutes. The text reproduced here is the original, slightly longer, version and therefore differs slightly from that which was actually delivered. CGJ

Sqn Ldr Kellett's Wellesley (L2638) being worked on at Ismailia. The airman working on the engine (on the right, standing on a ladder) is LAC Jefford, C W (50072), the speaker's father

6. The Second World War

Squadron Leader Philip Saxon

Chairman's Introduction:

Now to deal with the rapid advances that were made during World War 2 we have Squadron Leader Philip Saxon. He served in the Royal Air Force from 1941 to 1946, during which time he did a great deal of flying, mainly with Ferry Command, all over the Mediterranean and Africa and out to India. After demobilisation he read Mathematics and History at Cambridge; followed by 36 years in industry. he is a marathon runner and swimmer; and is now researching a History of Specialist Navigation in the RAF . . . Philip . . .

World War Two represents a relatively short span in the history of the RAF; but it saw an enormous leap forward in the practise – and the theory – of air navigation. I shall identify two main areas of development which were remarkable by any standards: – the introduction of improved aids to navigation, and particularly the electronic aids; the latter, we should remember, being largely confined to North West Europe; – and, no less remarkable, the training of the observers and navigators; which improved so dramatically in both quality and quantity during the course of the war.

At the beginning the boffins had other priorities, principally the 'defence of the realm'. But the training issue seemed to be the more immediate and the expansion in numbers had begun before the outbreak of war, although only a few had realised at that stage the inadequacy of navigational standards. Meanwhile, the task of training the vast numbers of aircrew who would be required (many of whom had never seen an aircraft at close quarters) would call on all the organisational and administrative resources of the Service.

The direct-entry observer of 1939 (the 5-8-0s), following his initial kitting-out and square-bashing, generally attended a Civilian Air Navigation School for a three-month course, with civilian pilots and instructors, many of the latter being ex-mariners without actual air navigation experience. The syllabus covered the traditional subjects of Maps and Charts, Magnetism and Compasses, Instruments, Signals, Meteorology and Dead Reckoning; but no

Astro. Total flying time was about 35 hours, in Ansons, and was largely concerned with map-reading and elementary Dead Reckoning: the two or three night cross-countries tended to have major towns as turning points (this was before the black-out). Then came a month of air gunnery and bombing before operational training in the Reserve Squadrons for a further four months or so; with about 60 hours in the air (some 25 of which was at night). All this was not great preparation for taking a bomber over the Ruhr.

But there were better things on the horizon. AVM Wilf Oulton, an instructor at the School of Air Navigation at Manston in the years preceding the war, has stressed the importance of the study in depth carried out there into the methodology of astro navigation. Over the years the School had been the centre of astro expertise; but this had remained a specialist subject, and there was now an effort to bring the techniques within the reach of the ordinary squadron navigator. The climax of this was a three-week course on the subject, – initially for pilots; since some of the squadrons still held their second pilots to be responsible for the navigation of the aircraft. In the longer term this initiative by Manston was to bring the invaluable techniques of astro navigation into the basic training of the navigator.

In the early months of the war the navigational role of the second pilot led to the misemployment of observers on some operational squadrons, which were still established for two pilots per crew. When the Wellingtons of 99 Squadron flew over the German Fleet in the daylight sortie of December, 1939, two of the twelve crews were each carrying two Sergeant observers; and one of those aircraft was amongst those lost. Yet as one second pilot on that day told me 'some of the observers flew as air gunners and others purely as observers, that is, looking out of the astrodome'. But some were allowed, at least, to participate in the navigation. Another second pilot commented that 'I had been back at the nav's table for about the last half-hour of the action preparing a course for home from Sergeant Parton's (the observer) excellent air plot, whilst he was in the astrodome giving a superbly calm, controlling commentary on the direction of the fighter attacks for our air gunners'.

In the build-up to the outbreak of war, the role of the observer had been given increased official recognition, (as we have heard). In war-time it was intended that he would be of equal standing to the pilot; but it did not quite happen like that. No observers were commissioned until the Spring of 1940: John Mitchell (the first observer to reach Air rank) recalls that on arrival at his Battle O.T.U. in April, 1940, he was an object of some curiosity since he was the first commissioned observer they had seen. The improvement in the status of the navigator was to be a gradual process. The position, in fact, is probably best summed up in an excerpt from a paper written for the Air Navigation Committee in early 1943, by Group Captains Kelly Barnes and David Waghorn who stated that 'At the beginning of the war the standard of navigation in the Service was infinitely lower than it should have been. The only officers with anything like an adequate knowledge of the subject were those who had taken the Long Navigation course. They had been trained in very small numbers, were classified as specialists and were commonly regarded as 'cranks'. As a matter of interest the total number of RAF officers who had graduated as Spec.Ns between 1920 and 1939 was only just over 100: by comparison war-time expansion increased the figure to more than 150 at Port Albert in 1942 alone. During the whole war many hundreds of navigators received specialist training to a level that would have seemed impossible a few years before.

It had been realised before the outbreak of war that a cramped and vulnerable island offered limited resources for flying training and the process had been put in train to negotiate what has been called 'one of the most brilliant pieces of imaginative organisation ever conceived': which bore fruit in the agreement with Dominion Governments to set up the Empire Air Training Scheme. The agreement was signed on 17 December, 1939, and training began in April, 1940. Ultimately, between 1940 and 1945, that scheme trained some 200,000 aircrew overseas, including over 40,000 navigators. Of these Canada trained almost two-thirds and South Africa nearly a quarter. This remarkable total does not include those trained wholly in the UK in the early part of the war: – and during this period the level of training improved dramatically.

First ITW – remember Torquay, Babbacombe and the rest? Here the concentration was on physical fitness, drill and signalling; not forgetting the endless sessions of aircraft recognition. I recall being on guard duty on the front at Torquay when I saw a plane approaching: it was when the bomb fell away and I saw the swastikas that I instantly recognised it as an Me 109 – from a prone position, of course! At ITW we had a marching pace of 140 to the minute, and were known as Critchley's Greyhounds. It is a point of interest that in 1918 the man in charge of initial training for the RAF had been none other than Brigadier General Critchley (later a founder of the Greyhound Racing Association).

Then there was Elementary Air Navigation School at Eastbourne, which provided an intensive four-week course introducing cadets to the various aspects of navigational theory, including Astro. The bubble sextant was first used on the roof of the Grand Hotel (no wonder it later got five stars!). This course was devised and set up in 1941 by a Wing Commander Don Bennett; being his first job on re-joining the RAF after his spell as a civilian on the North Atlantic Ferry operation. It was not the least of his contributions to the cause of navigation.

Air Navigation School was a further three months covering an impressive syllabus, and providing more than 100 hours flying. Back home the Advanced Flying Units, set up by Edward Chilton, provided a four-week course enabling the observer to familiarise himself with flying conditions in the UK – blackout, balloon barrages, weather and all (and particularly the weather!). Then on to the OTUs, which had been formed from the original Reserve Squadrons. Over the entire training period, which lasted rather a long time by that stage, the total flying hours were of the order of 220, with about 50 at night: and one had, hopefully, managed at least one three-star fix with a very small cocked hat. I have detailed this training sequence somewhat to demonstrate the great improvement that had been achieved in a relatively short space of time.

But this great training effort required a substantial increase in the quantity and quality of instructors: and this had to be balanced against the increasing number of navigational staff appointments, requiring officers with qualifications previously considered the perquisite of the specialist navigator. An example relates to the field of operational requirements, where all aspects of navigation other than personnel and training had been the responsibility of one Wing Commander, which was now expanded to three sections each headed up by a Group Captain. Moreover it was necessary to preserve a cadre of experienced and competent navigators in the operational units. The specialisation of aircrew duties helped a bit, by cutting out the distraction of bombing and air-gunnery: and, in an attempt to maintain standards, it was ruled that navigators should alternate between flying and administrative and instructional duties.

At the start of the war the Air Navigation School at Manston had moved westward to St Athan, and expanded the number of their courses substantially. Instructor courses were provided for those entering the Service from civilian life with previous navigation experience and astro-extension courses continued. All this helped to diffuse better standards, not only in the training establishments but also in the operational units. But the fall of France resulted in the disruption of the training schedule due to frequent air raids, and it became apparent that effective training could not be carried out under these conditions. Specialist navigation training, therefore, was moved to Port Albert in Canada in October 1940 and the short courses went to Cranage in Cheshire. Of Cranage someone later wrote 'Nowhere could a worse location for a navigational school have been found. It was ringed by balloon areas; awash most of the time, with miserable housing and mess facilities, in the midst of an area of industrial haze and close to chemical works. But it was the best that could be offered'. That having been said, it must be added that the fact that the staff at Cranage, at the insistence of Kelly Barnes, was of a high academic and wide operational experience tended to offset its geographical deficiencies.

Let me leave training for now, and deal with the technical aspects of navigational development. During the first couple of years or so of the war navigation in the operational Commands was, to say the least, very hit-or-miss, and rather more miss than hit. Dependence on Dead Reckoning and Astro, when the conditions permitted, was not always adequate. Over the UK one useful visual aid was provided by the flashing beacons, or lighthouses, which had been resurrected from World War One: and over the Continent the more able observers exploited the German night-fighter MF beacons with some success, and were briefed on those left unjammed by 90 Group. But help was at hand: and early in 1942 the first British hyperbolic navigation aid (Gee) became available. The virtue of Gee was that it was simple to use and it produced a very accurate fix in about one minute (compare this with the time it took to obtain a three-star fix). At height its range was 300 miles or so; but it was subject to jamming. Amongst other things it did provide an excellent homing device. The American LORAN system, based on similar principles but using medium-wave frequencies rather than VHF, was invaluable on the Transatlantic route with its greater range.

Aircraft radar aids that were developed had the advantage of being operated independently of ground stations. Coastal Command had operated airborne radar (ASV) since 1940: now, by the end of 1942, an advanced system had been produced and with it the Bomber Command version, which was code-named H2S. These aids distinguished ground – and water – features; but they required a degree of expertise to achieve the best results. Other systems came along such as OBOE, which was ground-controlled, and GH (Grid Homing, I believe) and these were used as blind-bombing devices, often providing greater accuracy than visual bomb-aiming. We also put the German SONNE radio beam system to our own use as CONSOL.

Complementing these valuable navigational fixing aids, new Dead Reckoning instruments were devised. The Air Position Indicator provided a back-up to the navigator's own air plot; and was reset when he got a fix. A modified set was introduced later which could be sited over the navigation table such that, when the plotting chart was aligned correctly, a pinpoint of light moving over the chart indicated the still-air position of the aircraft. A further development enabled the wind velocity (calculated or forecast) to be entered, thus producing the Ground Position Indicator.

But we must bear in mind that these remarkable aids were known only to those navigators flying in the European theatre of operations. Those of us overseas, and particularly in the Middle and Far East, were dependent on the more traditional methods of navigation. On ferry work, of course, you had to attune your navigational techniques to the type of aircraft and equipment that you collected (and a lot of these were American, which did not necessarily have standard RAF equipment). However, tribute must be paid to the work of David Waghorn, as DDOR (Nav), and others who influenced U.S. production through the British Air Commission in Washington to achieve increasing standardisation of instrumentation and layout as the war progressed.

Flying in the Near and Middle East, in fact, over vast stretches of featureless desert was somewhat similar to flying over the sea (although we did not lob out smoke bombs for drift taking). Visibility was often excellent, and a hand-held compass was useful for obtaining a running fix on the occasional recognisable, and perhaps distant, landmark. Flying from Delta to Habb, one had the advantage of the finest navigational aid in those parts – the pipeline that ran straight across the desert for some 300 miles. This followed the original track, laid out in 1921, that has been referred to earlier. From the navigator's point of view it was a case of 'for this relief much thanks'.

Whilst weather conditions in the Middle East were generally good, the same could not be said about the Far East. The monsoon period, in particular, posed specific hazards and the maps out there were even less reliable than those in the Middle East. In the winter night bombing was the rule; but in the monsoon period the bomber squadrons had to resort to intruder patrols along the Burmese coast. Radio assistance was virtually non-existent and the navigator had to maintain his air plot and depend on DR. It was a matter of careful flight planning; and flying at 500 feet over the Bay of Bengal with the occasional drift reading on the white horses, and certain pinpoints that you learnt to depend on. Map-reading in the Ganges Delta area, with the constantly changing maze of waterways, was not easy and, on the whole, this provided one of the most testing navigational challenges of all.

But in our review of navigation in war-time conditions we must not forget the pilots who flew alone (without the sparkling company of a navigator!), and who developed the skills of air pilotage to a remarkable degree. An excellent example is provided by Hugh Verity, who landed his Lysander on a minimal flare-path in France on numerous occasions. At a Society meeting some years ago he described his navigational methods; and what it really came down to, apart from the application of common sense, was meticulous pre-flight planning and accurate flying. The very factors, I would suggest, that are the basis of all good navigation. In this context, of course, the PR pilots carried brilliant air pilotage into long-range operations.

In September, 1942, there was an official change of title from observer to navigator, marked by the introduction of the 'N' brevet: not altogether a popular move amongst the 'O's. Meanwhile, increasing numbers were under-going advanced training at Port Albert and Cranage. Port Albert had been fairly churning out the Spec.Ns; over a period of three years or so fifteen Specialist courses graduated, in addition to many short courses – particularly Astro. Many of the Spec.Ns returned to the UK on ferry duties across the North Atlantic. But Port Albert was rather a long way from the action and tended to drift further from current practise as, increasingly, navigational expertise resided with the operational Commands in the UK. The new electronic devices could not be made available over there, for security and other reasons. Accordingly, in 1943, all specialist navigation training was centralised at Cranage.

One fascinating item of development at Port Albert related to the Celestial Navigation Trainer, devised by the talented American engineer – Ed Link, whom most will recall for his Link Trainer. The Celestial Navigation Trainer comprised a fuselage set in something like a planetarium, with the star dome rotating to correspond with the time anywhere in the Northern Hemisphere. The speed of the aircraft could be varied, as could the latitude and longitude. Later in the war some models were produced in Britain, at Elstree. In retrospect, its main claim to fame lay in the input that it made to the problems of plotting in high latitudes. It was used, for example, for training purposes by the navigators of the first Aries flight. With his new-found interest in Astro, Ed Link dreamed up a series of Star Identification Charts but this was nothing as mundane as the RAF version. To produce his charts some nubile models, wearing a few sparkling stars strategically placed, posed in appropriate attitudes to produce the correct shapes of the constellations. It was said that they were very popular – the charts, that is – and that (and here I quote) 'few RAF navigators thereafter forgot the position of the stars'. If you believe that then you will believe anything!

In late 1942 Cranage, now the Central Navigation School, commenced the Staff Navigation courses, as a development of its former courses with a syllabus akin to that of the old Specialist course. The new title was in token of the fact that the graduate was fully capable of filling any of the large number of staff appointments to which it was formerly necessary to post a Spec N. In addition a new series of Specialist courses were introduced for experienced navigators with a degree in mathematics, or its equivalent, the aim being to extend navigational knowledge and simplify its application. In early 1943 three-week Specialist Refresher courses were intro-duced to update previous graduates. Staff Navigation courses were also set up in both Canada and South Africa.

The resources of Cranage were now very stretched indeed, and the C.N.S. moved to Shawbury early in 1944. Over the next few years Shawbury was to become the centre of navigational excellence; later that year it took on the title of Empire Air Navigation School under the command of Philip Mackworth, a legendary Spec.N, with Dickie Richardson as his deputy. Some time after he had produced his revised version of the Air Navigation Manual (AP 1234), Dickie had become the Chief Navigation Officer for Coastal Command. There he and his staff formulated a navigation drill dictating a minimum hourly input of activities by the navigator. This helped to set operating standards and simplified post-flight analysis; and thereby enabled Squadron and Group navigation Officers to enforce good navigation practise, and to identify the weaker brethren in need of further training. Subsequently, both Bomber and Transport Commands adopted the approach, modified to meet their own requirements. Later, of course, there were Nav. Leaders, along with Leaders of other aircrew functions, to help improve standards in their respective disciplines.

A summary of the drills in use in the later stages of the war serves to illustrate the manner in which navigation routines had developed over only a very few years. It is axiomatic that a comprehensive flight plan be prepared. As a basis for accurate track-keeping Coastal Command laid down an hourly drill requiring 4 drifts, 1 three-drift W/V, 1 fix or M.P.P. (Most Probable Position) and one recommencement of the airplot. The maintenance of a trackplot was also recommended, as was regular checking of the compasses by astro compass.

The main features of Bomber Command navigation were held to be track-keeping and accurate E.T.A.s, to ensure that the bomber force operated in a compact group. Bomber Command drills distinguished between H2S and non-H2S squadrons, with the former usually forming the vanguard. The H2S squadrons, who carried a plotter in addition to the navigator, were required to determine wind velocities at frequent intervals and transmit them to base; where they were vetted and re-transmitted to the main force as zephyr winds. These winds, by definition, were invariably accurate, but if there were errors then the main force would not lose its cohesion. For the non-H2S aircraft the chief aid was Gee, but zephyr winds were to be used when available. Timing was to take precedence over track-keeping. It was said that the navigator in Bomber Command depended on his radar aids, and might occasionally use a D/F fix: but some did use astro; and Polaris, for obvious reasons, was a firm favourite. Analysis of the raids tended to deal with the dispersal of the aircraft along the route; and it was noted that the grouping of aircraft deteriorated on the return journey (which should not have occasioned any surprise).

Transport Command drills were, of necessity, less specific; since the conditions were very variable. Procedures tended to be laid down which left the navigator free to select the most suitable methods. A long sea crossing, for example, whether by day or night or in temperate or tropical regions had its own appropriate – and flexible – drills. The crossing of the South Atlantic en route to Takoradi, for example, was planned such that a 'noon' fix could be obtained in order to facilitate landfall on the West African coast; and one usually aimed to port of track on that leg (remember the shape of the coast). The navigator in Transport Command tended to rely more on astro: but when flying over areas where map-reading was relatively simple one was discouraged from using it to the exclusion of all else. Analysis of flights also had to be flexible, and the navigator was judged by the results obtained rather than the actual methods used.

Over the Royal Air Force as a whole the analysis and control of air navigation helped to improve standards of performance of the majority of navigators; and this was an immense achievement in such a brief time. In 1944, it was at last recognised that a single co-ordinating voice was needed at the proper level in the Air Ministry to wield the necessary influence on behalf of air navigation as a whole. Accordingly a Directorate of Navigation and Control was set up on the staff of the Vice-Chief of Air Staff. Meanwhile Shawbury offered its Specialist and Staff Navigation courses at a very high standard; and the reputation of the School was world-wide. In May 1945 this was underlined by the flights of Aries 1 over the North Geographic and Magnetic Poles; the ultimate navigational challenge. There were five Spec.Ns aboard (one of whom is with us here today, I believe) and it represented a great step forward in the techniques of polar navigation. It epitomised the dramatic progress in the field of navigation that the RAF had made during the course of World War Two. You will be hearing more about Aries flights after lunch.

7. *Morning Discussion Period*

Chairman's Introduction:

As one would expect, not only have we enjoyed a morning of excellent lectures but they have also arrived at their destination exactly on time. It is now 12.15 and those who have talked to us this morning, and myself, will congregate on the stage to answer any of your questions; so a quick shuffle and then we will start . . .

Gp Capt HANS NEUBROCH: In May 1943 I was one of the last people to be commissioned as an observer. My second Station Commander, at Mount Hope, was B. K. Burnett, who had – as a pre-war Spec.N – navigated one of the Wellesleys from Ismailia to Darwin. In 1970, when he was the last British C-in-C, Far East, I accompanied him on a flight from Singapore to the American islands in the Eastern Pacific. We refuelled at Darwin, commanded then by Ralph Glassop, RAAF, an aborigine who had been a fighter ace in Korea. He asked Air Chief Marshal Burnett whether he had been to Darwin before, and Burnett said "Yes, indeed." Glassop pressed on, "How did you get here, sir?" and Burnett answered "I found my own way!"

Gp Capt COLIN PARRY (RIN): We have had some excellent presentations, but all tending to criticise navigation between the Wars. I wonder if it is fair to do that; because then the airframes themselves were not up to it. Those of us who have tried taking astro at 2,000 feet know that it is much easier at 20,000 feet, or higher. With astro being such a limited aid in the aircraft of the time would one not expect any effort to be put into developing it; to answer my own question. The same is true of things like DF; because the hull of the aircraft would have had to be earthed and bonded. Would the Panel like to comment?

Wg Cdr JEFFORD: Work began on airborne DF in 1917, and by 1918 a reliable system had been designed; consisting of two loops wound at 90 degrees, about five feet tall, rotating and fixed inside the rear fuselage of a Handley-Page 0/400. Trenchard was not terribly interested, so the Independent Force never really used it. Eventually an aeroplane was flown from Biggin Hill to Paris blind, then back the next day, using this system; which excited much interest. Had the War gone on another few months I am sure that it would have been introduced. A.P.s published in 1920/21 showed it, with photographs and wiring diagrams; but by 1922 the whole thing had just disappeared.

With astro, at a specialist level, technical development of navigation was happening. But, until 1933, British Defence Policy said that there would not be a war for ten years, and this was annually renewable. The job of the RAF was to be a cheap means of policing the Empire; and there was no need for high-tech navigation. Operations were carried out in daylight, generally in fair weather, overseas. When the rise of the European dictatorships came in 1933, then people like Waghorn began to say 'we are not very good at this'. The Long Ns had the technical knowledge, but that was the impetus for developing systems for the Sergeant Observer to use.

Flt Lt ALEC AYLIFFE: There were so few people actually navigating that the experience needed was not there. DF, for example was a bit of a bind: one system operated from the ground, so that you transmitted and they gave you a bearing – and around the North Sea in WWI you could get a fix within 50 to 60 miles, if you were lucky; which might get you home. The other systems, of course, were the expensive loop aerials which came after 1918: they put them in the wings, and you had to turn the aircraft towards the station to get a bearing, and home on to it. It did not catch on, and no-one had any interest in developing easier methods for the squadron pilot. The Spec.Ns, as Kelly Barnes said, were seen as cranks; an interest in navigation was seen as being a bit odd.

Wg Cdr PETER WILLIAMS: How did techniques compare with the German Naval Services? I can recall one Zeppelin that attempted to bomb through cloud whilst flying at considerable height. They used navigational fixes of a sort, and developed air-pressure pads. When Strasser, the Captain, was shot down off Yarmouth he was actually contemplating bombing America.

DAVID PAGE: The Imperial German Navy's Zeppelin navigation seems to have been excellent. A few years ago we had one of the Luftwaffe's leading lights – Dr Karworth – over here. During the War he had interrogated captured Allied navigators and was one of the most pro-RAF navigation chaps I had ever come across. He felt that the Luftwaffe relied too much on radio systems, and should have used more astro. It may, of course, have been a case of the grass being greener on the other side.

AM SIR JOHN CURTISS: An interesting point. Do we have anybody who knows what techniques the Hindenberg used to cross the Atlantic? They also did round the world flights in airships: and what about the great explorers, like Amelia Earhart, who attempted round the world?

ALEC AYLIFFE: In 1911 they had a decent compass in their airships, which was Top Secret. By 1918 it was quite clear that their navigation was pretty variable and that some crews were relying too much on DF bearings. In airship flights in the inter-war years they used the standard navigation techniques of the day. The RAF had good contacts with the international community; and Hughes was desperately trying to flog the RE MkV bubble sextant to the Italians, who were about the only people interested in it. Coutinho, the Portuguese Admiral who flew across the South Atlantic, made some significant developments in sextants. There were some good achievements by the Australians, and Quantas; also Pan-Am. Quite a few RAF navigators learnt their skills at the Pan-Am school in Miami in the early 1940s. It is wrong to say that the RAF were behind the times: the techniques were publicised and practised, only they were used by the specialists and not by your average pilot.

AVM JOHN DOWNEY: This business of crossing the Atlantic. Between Alcock and Brown in 1919 and the outbreak of war in 1939, leaving aside the trial flights of Imperial Airways and Pan-Am in the late 1930s with four-engined aeroplanes, the ordinary flyer with one or two engines made about 110 attempts to cross the North Atlantic; in both directions. A little under half made it and 41 people died, the last two in 1939. Navigation was mostly taking off from New York and heading East! People set off for Berlin and finished up in Norway, or Paris and ended up in Spain. Lindbergh had a high-tech compass, but no radio: he could have – but he chose petrol. Keep going as long as possible and you will eventually hit something. Lindbergh did not do a great deal of navigation, and did not try to make corrections once he was half-way across.

JEFFORD: Lindbergh frightened himself! The professional navigators were quite contemptuous of these 'stunt' flyers, who did not even follow track and just picked a heading and flew across.

DOWNEY: We should remember that almost everything was neglected between the Wars. One's wireless operator was an LAC from the signals section who had done practically no flying; and gunners were from the armaments section with, perhaps, no gunnery training. We had the Trenchard doctrine of bombing, but we had done no weapon effects tests to speak of; nor force requirement calculations. I was half-way through my FTS when the War started, training with Hart variants. Because the Hawker Fury had guns firing through the propeller we spent hours learning the details of the Constantinescu interrupter gear. I can remember the pressure in the reservoir to this day! It isn't any good to me now, and it wasn't then. I don't think that anybody had revised the training syllabuses since the year dot.

Fl Lt WANSBROUGH-WHITE: I have used the CSC and Dalton, which was mentioned this morning and I have actually got a CDC; but if anybody can explain to me how it works I will be eternally grateful. Also, a historic question – the Dalton computer – on the back is the logarithmic, or Appleyard Scale. Who were Dalton and Appleyard?

JEFFORD: Commander Rollo Appleyard, RNAS, had a bent for adapting maritime navigation techniques for aviation; he invented the Scale.

AYLIFFE: Philip Dalton was an American inventor whose main developments were 8 or 9 marks of this dead-reckoning computer; but he was just one of many. I have with me a French Navigation Manual from 1928 which covers a variety of circular abacuses; and Weems U.S. editions of his works has whole chapters on them. He had a vast collection of Course and Distance calculators, right up to the modern ones. They all work on roughly the same principle, and I have the instructions if you want to see them later.

Sq Ldr DAVID NUTTING: Just a quick comment on the relative seniority of navigators. I am reliably informed by an ex-captain of a Mosquito that in Polish squadrons in the RAF the navigator was the captain of the aircraft.

Cdr TONY FANNING (RIN): I would like to add the Distant Reading Compass to the list of instruments not available in 1939. It was invented in 1926 followed by lengthy development work at Farnborough, but did not get into operational service until '41 or '42 in Stirlings. We had to manage with normal dead-beat, before the Americans came in with their Pioneers, Bendixes and others. The DR Compass was a splendid thing but it was monstrous, and smaller aircraft did what they could with the dead-beat compass; which had been developed way back in 1918 by Cdr Campbell and Dr Bennett of the Admiralty Compass Observatory.

JOHN DAVIS: What truth, if any, is there in the tale that went round in the 1942-43 period that American navigation was appalling?

Sq Ldr PHILIP SAXON: When I was at OTU an American squadron of fighters landed one evening to ask where they were; so we put them up for the night and had a party. They hadn't long been in the UK.

AYLIFFE: The Americans had much the same funding and incentive problems as the RAF. They had a few specialist navigators and all the knowledge, but not a great deal of experience; and they will admit cheerfully that in 1942 they were as badly off as we were in 1939.

(NOTE: A contribution on this topic from Edgar Spridgeon, who was naturally not able to give it at the time, is attached)

AM SIR FREDERICK SOWREY: Would the team care to comment on Air Staff policy from, say, 1934 onwards and its effect on air navigation? If our bombing policy was predicated to be formations of aircraft operating in close support as, for example, the December '39 raids on Wilhelmshaven by Wellingtons, who found their target adequately by daylight, would that not have influenced policy towards that type of operation, not realising that the majority of later operations would, force majeure, be carried out by single aircraft at night.

JEFFORD: Between the Wars we painted our Virginias and Hyderabads dark green, in order to fly as singletons to the same place at night. The idea of the self-defending bomber force really stemmed from WWI when the Independent Force had not only the Handley-Pages but also single-engined DH9s. These day bombers flew in formation, and successfully defended themselves with single gunners in the back to produce concentrated fire – and it worked: a night bomber operated by itself. Any aeroplane might be required to fly by night and, notionally, everybody ought to have been able to navigate. In the 1920s, there simply was not the threat to persuade people to spend money on production; although the theory and the technology were there.

AYLIFFE: Why, with a policy which relied on the air offensive, did they not take positive steps to ensure that it could be maintained effectively in wartime? It was not just navigation; bombing and other aircraft trades were also neglected. The implications of Trenchard's Air Force Doctrine were not really thought through: after all, these were not Trenchard's strengths. I think that if we have anything to learn from this episode in RAF history it is that doctrine should come from what you can do.

AVM WILFRID OULTON: It might help if I tried to describe the atmosphere in the Royal Air Force between the Wars: I do not think that there are many of my contemporaries here to argue with me! The total emphasis was on the Air Defence of Great Britain. Every pilot wanted to be a fighter pilot, except for one or two – including me. The best aeroplanes and tactics were for the defence of the country because, in the national consciousness, in the 1914-18 War the things to worry about had been the Zeppelin and Gotha raids. So it was the second-class citizens who went into bombers or coastal and the bright boys all went into fighters, which operated at short-range and did not really need navigation. It was this attitude that brought about a complete disregard for navigation; so that things like the Distant Reading Compass took 14 or 15 years from start to finish.

It was 1938 before the penny began to drop. I was given the job of telling twelve senior fighter squadron commanders about navigation. They were all hoary WWI types or brilliant people, and I was absolutely terrified of them; I was only a Flight Lieutenant. I thought, how on earth am I going to begin addressing these very senior and knowledgeable chaps; I shall get my bottom kicked. So, like Caesar, I devised a stratagem. I put them in a lecture room and said "Gentlemen, it is ridiculous for me to attempt to teach you anything about navigation; you obviously know all about it. But we have to go through the formalities of the course, so you will do an exercise tomorrow. Each of you will be put into an Anson, with a pilot and a wireless operator and you will please fly to the Terschelling light-vessel off the coast of Holland; take a photograph and bring it back to me. The pilot will follow your instructions implicitly unless the safety of the aircraft is involved". I am happy to say that not one of them got back to Manston: and from that moment onwards they began to listen.

I have been fascinated by some of the nostalgia. Regarding Dalton

Computers, for example; I spent some of my own money on one, and very valuable it was too. I must congratulate Philip Saxon on his excellent presentation. Oh, one more thing: you asked how some of the long-range flights were achieved. Well, in Suva, Fiji, I once met – not Wiley Post himself – but his navigator, whose name I can't remember.

FLOOR: Gatty.

OULTON: I had a long talk with him and said: "How did you manage on that first San Franscisco to Hawaii flight?" He said, "First of all we flew to a point well north of Hawaii where, by a sort of longitude shot I knew pretty well where I was; then I made him circle for an hour and a half until I could get my noon shot, and be quite sure whether to fly north or south. We flew south and there was Hawaii".

Prof SIDNEY BRANDON: The successful Transatlantic crossings between the Wars included one by a man called Corrigan, who set out from New York bound for California but flew a reciprocal bearing! But I really wanted to ask about Chichester's influence on astro navigation practice in the RAF.

CURTISS: I am delighted that someone has brought that up. One of the things that inspired me to take an interest in navigation was that marvellous book 'Alone over the Tasman Sea'. Francis Chichester in a Gypsy Moth, using a hand-held marine sextant, managed to navigate himself to Earl Howe Island and then eventually reach the coast of Australia. I was told that he had quite a lot of influence on the development of navigational training.

JEFFORD: Certainly Chichester's reliability, planning and logistics were at fault in crossing the Tasman and he got himself out of trouble by an innovative use of navigation. He knew that his compass was unreliable, and he had not got a landing compass so that he couldn't swing it. He had changed his undercarriage for floats, which had not improved his compass. If he flew to his point target over the sea he would not know where he was, so he simply aimed off to the right and when his ETA ran out he turned left; and there was his island. I was interested to hear that that was what Wiley Post had done. Chichester checked his ETA with astro, and I associate him with astro but I am not sure what direct influence he had in the RAF.

AYLIFFE: He was a Flight Lieutenant at Air Ministry when he assisted Squadron Leader Dickie Richardson with the revision of AP

1234; you can see his influence in the chapters on astro. He was very short-sighted, incidentally, and there was no question of his flying in the RAF. Chichester's last fix before he flew across the Tasman was 60 miles in error, but he still continued. He claimed to have invented the airplot, but looking at his log and chart and considering navigation at the time, I think that this claim is a little far-fetched.

(One interesting point regarding Chichester's service in the RAF during the War was that, despite his formidable reputation in air navigation, he was initially refused permission to wear the brevet on the grounds that he had not passed the requisite courses. Following representations on his behalf permission was eventually forth-coming.– Saxon).

RALPH FELLOWS: I was an observer, trained in England. I wonder if I can get any information on the Astrograph?

AVM JACK FURNER: I used the Astrograph quite a lot in Stirlings. It was a device about two feet above the navigation table, projecting lines of equal altitude for two stars at any one time; add Polaris and you get a three-star fix. It was a very useful gadget, but you had to line it up very accurately with your plotting chart.

FELLOWS: I used it, but I wondered what had happened to it?

PARRY: I think that there are two answers to that. First, the astro-graph was more time consuming than using the standard reduction tables of the time. A competent navigator could reduce a sight in about three minutes; whereas setting up the machine was all-important. You had a little stick to give you the correct height above the chart table; because if you did not have the longitude and height correct the errors could be enormous. The other thing was that the Astrograph was a late comer; and was already being overtaken by Inertial Navigation Systems, and so forth. It was a nice idea, but it did not really have the clout to carry on into the future.

A POSSIBLE SUPPLEMENTARY ANSWER to the question at the Seminar regarding the alleged poor navigation ability of American pilots on arrival in this country.

I was a member of the ARNOLD SCHEME in the United States and was trained as a Pilot by the U.S. Army Air Force and, after receiving my 'Wings' in August 1942, I remained in Alabama instructing American Cadets to 'Wings' standard at an Advanced Flying School.

Having checked my Log Book I find that my navigation training started at 'Basic School' where we were flying the Vultee 'Valiant' BT-13A. With a total of 110 hours 'under my belt' I was taken on a dual 'X-Country', 150 miles each way. This was followed by one solo, one dual, one solo by day, and one solo at night – the total hours being 7½ by day and 2 by night. At an 'Advanced School' flying the AT-6 (Harvard) leading to 'Graduation', I had only one dual trip of 2 hours followed by five solo by day and three solo by night, with total hours 9 by day and 6¼ by night.

When I was instructing U.S. Cadets, I am sure that they received a similar sequence of training to develop their skill in going places and getting back.

The shock they must have had on arriving over this country must have been overwhelming to most of them. Firstly, the climate; most of the training in the USA was carried out in the 'Sunshine Belt' of the Southern States where very good conditions could be relied upon for most of the time. I well remember night X-C's with triangular routes having 90 mile legs when it was possible to see the 'glow' in the sky from an Army Camp near to Base from nearly all points on the track. Then there were 'light-lines' (beacons flashing every 20 miles along airways) and Radio 'Beams' to assist in times of need. This is where I first heard of 'C.A.V.U.' in Met briefing and the briefings were usually very reliable.

Secondly, the topography. Few towns, so not easily confusing and most, even small ones, having a water tower with the name written on it in large letters. Rail tracks dead straight for many miles, thus providing as good a guidance system as the line ploughed across the desert! Even small towns having 'landing strips, usually identifiable.

Compare all this with the UK. At night – darkness. No 'light-lines', no town lights (a 'blackout' was enforced by law!). Except in a 'good summer', unreliable weather, and bad weather made worse in many areas by industrial smoke and pollution. And in so many parts of the country, railway lines lying around like 'spilled spaghetti' and no water tanks or railway stations proudly displaying their names. (Many cadets in the U.S. were known to pretend they were unsure of their position as an excuse to 'Buzz' the railroad station to read the name.)

Perhaps these are some of the reasons why we should have felt sorry for our allies who had to learn a new way of life when flying over the United Kingdom.

Edgar Spridgeon   15 November, 1996

8. The Aries Flights

Group Captain David Broughton

Chairman's Introduction

We have dealt with the period leading up to World War 2 and we have also dealt with the great advances that were made during that war; so we now come into the post-war period and to lead the way we are going to talk about the Aries flights. We have a real expert on the subject here – Group Captain David Broughton. He spent 31 years in the RAF as a navigator and a staff officer in a wide range of posts dealing with research and policy into navigation systems and weapon fields. He is now the Director of the Royal Institute of Navigation, and a specialist lecturer in Navigation at Nottingham University. More important, from the point of view of his subject, David has flown on 23 Aries flights – of which 21 reached the North Geographic Pole. Perhaps he will tell us about the other two as well! . . . David . . .

No record of navigation within the Royal Air Force would be complete without a mention of the Aries flights, which span half a century and are still mounted for the benefit of GD Aerosystems students, the research agencies and industry.

By 1944 RAF navigation training was centred on Shawbury, whose wide remit was reflected in its title as of late 1944 – 'Empire Air Navigation School'. By then the School was charged not only with training RAF and allied navigators, but also with carrying out research and promulgating navigation doctrine throughout the Commonwealth. Many routine training and demonstration flights embraced destinations as far afield as Canada and Ceylon and the Shawbury fleet included an impressive 42 Wellingtons and 4 Stirlings as well as a spattering of smaller aircraft.

ARIES I

But an aircraft with longer range was needed and a brand-new Lancaster Mk 1, PD328, was acquired in September 1944. It was one of 200 built by Metropolitan-Vickers and assembled by Avro at Woodford. The aircraft was actually delivered to the Avro Repair Unit at RAF Waddington, where the dorsal gun turret was replaced by a second astrodome, but otherwise it looked like any other Lancaster, retaining its original camouflage.

In October 1944, *'Aries'*, as the aircraft was now called, undertook the first RAF circumnavigation of the world under the command of Wg Cdr McKinley, a pilot on the School's staff, with Sqn Ldr Davis as 1st navigator. It flew westwards with the intention of both passing on current navigation techniques to training establishments and operational squadrons, and of collecting data, especially from the U.S. and Pacific areas. It was also important to gather information on Lancaster operations in tropical conditions in light of possible raids against Japan; and not forgotten was the gleaning of data for future commercial routes. The trip was most successful and *Aries* returned after 53 days and over 200 flying hours, having made a series of 'firsts' and set a few records. These included Australia-UK in 72 hours, knocking over 50 hours off the forerunner.

By 1942 interest was growing in operating at high latitudes, and the arrival of *Aries* presented the possibility of putting theory into practice. Wg Cdr McKinley and Wg Cdr Maclure, a Canadian exchange navigator and RAF Spec N graduate, were the main instigators. The former was particularly interested in airframe and survival aspects and the latter had published a paper on associated orientation and navigation. This included the proposed adoption of the 'Greenwich' grid, a squared-up lattice within which Greenwich lies on a bearing of 000° from the North Geographical Pole. The grid was, of course, primarily devised to overcome the high latitude problem of convergence of the meridians at the Pole; this presented an impossible plotting task to the mechanical analogue computers of the day (and will even fool modern digital computers if not sensibly programmed). A series of simulated navigational exercises was conducted on the ground in a Link Celestial Navigation Trainer (the navigation equivalent of the more familiar pilots' Link Trainer, with collimated stars projected onto a surrounding dome) and aspects of flying techniques, maintenance, medical surveillance and survival were studied at great depth.

Meanwhile, late April 1945 saw *Aries* itself undergo some extensive modifications at RAF Waddington in preparation for Arctic flying. The nose and tail gun turrets were replaced by smooth fairings which gave it the appearance of the post-war civilianised version of the Lancaster, the Lancastrian. Additional fuel tanks were installed in the nose and bomb-bay, giving a full load of almost 4,000 gallons, and a Lincoln undercarriage was fitted to cope with the additional weight. The camouflage was also removed and the base metal polished. Four new Merlin XXIV engines were fitted by RAF mechanics. The entire transformation was completed in just nine days! *Aries* now boasted a range of about 5,000 miles; maximum take-off weight was 32 tons and typical cruising speed was 240 knots at 12,000 feet.

The *Aries* polar flights were not trying to create world firsts – short 'local' polar flights had been claimed from the mid-1920s – but they would constitute the first airborne comprehensive scientific investigations of the area and would represent the first British flight to the Pole. The aims were formidable – to test the new navigation techniques and examine crew efficiency; evaluate the navigation systems, especially compasses, DR systems and radar; conduct a magnetic survey in the area of the Magnetic Pole in northern Canada; obtain radar mapping and Loran photography; collect meteorological data; photograph Arctic topography; and record engine and airframe data. The list seemed endless.

An extensive navigation fit was installed, much of it by RAE Farnborough. Direct-reading compasses included the P10, B16, N1 and O1151A and these were joined by three distant-reading ones – the Air Ministry DRC and Pioneer flux-gate and Magnesyn types. An Admiralty-RAE 'special' horizontal-axis gyro was also fitted as the master gyro, together with two astro-compasses (one inverted), two Mk IXA sextants and a Link averaging octant. H2S Mk IIB mapping radar was carried and the standard large aircraft fit of navigation aids was on board; this included Gee, Loran AN/APN-4, T1154, R1155 and TR1196 radios, AYF and SCR 718 radio/radar altimeters, a modified API, AMI and Mk II drift recorder. RAE also fitted a flux-valve dip meter and 3-axis flux-valve magnetometer to determine dip and magnetic field strength. Much of the navigation and trials equipment was recorded on film at an 'auto-observer' position – a term still used in R&D flying.

Both position and heading information in the polar regions were to be highly reliant on the use of the sextant and astro-compass and in the permanent summer daylight at high-latitude it was deemed necessary for the sun and moon to lie on bearings of not less than 45° of each other to establish acceptable fixes. This would occur for only five consecutive days in May 1945 and thenceforth for lessening periods, and this largely dictated the window for the expedition. Navigation techniques were to be conventional up to 75°N, using a 1:2M Mercator chart; above 70°N transition to the Greenwich grid would be undertaken, using an astro-compass with the master gyro for steering and sextant for positioning on gridded polar stereographic charts – at 1:4M to 80°N and 1:2M to the Pole.

The crew for the polar flight, in addition to McKinley and Maclure (who coordinated research aspects), comprised Wg Cdr Anderson as senior navigator and observer for the plotter, Flt Lt Underwood as navigator/plotter, a co-pilot/engineer, two radio operators, three groundcrew and a doctor – 11 in all. All three navigators and both pilots were navigation specialists – indeed the two 'working' navigators were students of the current No 3 Spec N Course. Hot air cabin heating could not be used for fear of misting up the observation windows and electrical power could not be spared; hence personal warmth was provided by several layers of light clothing, with rotation of bodies to the front under the perspex cockpit for an occasional warm-up. Everyone on board was constantly breathing oxygen. The paucity of SAR facilities was recognised in the carriage of at least four weeks of emergency rations.

The leg to the Pole was to be attempted on 15 May and *Aries* left Shawbury for Meeks Field, Reykjavik, on 10 May – two days after VE Day. Time in Iceland was spent in resting, rehearsing high latitude techniques and sorting out the weather forecast; this proved a headache with only a half-dozen stations providing data for some 400,000 square miles of Arctic Basin. The final forecast led to a 24-hour delay, but another aircraft returned with favourable reports at 0100 on 16 May and *Aries* was airborne by 0300. Things did not go well, however, with persistent cloud to the east of Greenland causing dangerous icing which eventually precluded any possibility of reaching the Pole with sufficient reserves; *Aries* returned to Meeks Field nine hours after departure, having failed to reach the Pole.

Time was now of the essence; the acceptable sun-moon 'window' was soon to close and the Magnetic Pole was also to be visited. Hence, with confirmation from the forecasters that a more easterly route would be clearer, *Aries* was again airborne within a couple of hours, aiming initially for the island of Jan Mayen. There were still cloud and icing problems, but the broken ice of the polar region could be seen from 14,000 feet altitude on the final leg. The last run of 600 miles saw the navigators take 60 astro shots. The Pole was attained at 0206 on 17 May; the radio operator obtained a radio bearing from Reykjavik of due north, someone on board peeled a celebratory banana (a rarity in those days) and the doctor threw a union flag and bottle of beer overboard! A comparatively uneventful return saw the aircraft back at Reykjavik by 0900, almost 19 hours after becoming airborne on this second attempt.

There was little time for rest and at 0300 the next day *Aries* was off for the Magnetic Pole, planning to return to Dorval, Montreal. The Magnetic Pole's charted position was in the Boothia Peninsula in northern Canada, but the Astronomer Royal, who had been involved in the planning, believed it to be 200-300 miles further to the NNW. The flight proceeded across Greenland, and radar-altimeter soundings indicated that the ice-cap extended up to 8,500 feet above sea-level – but a generator failure forced an unscheduled diversion to Goose Bay. With less than 36 hours of sun-moon window remaining, feverish activity saw *Aries* airborne once more in the early hours of 19 May. This flight had to be managed as a maximum radius-of-action sortie with a return to Montreal when remaining fuel demanded. When the Boothia Peninsula was reached the dip angle was only 87° and the compasses pointed to the NNW, albeit sluggishly. A further 250 miles to the NNW saw dip increase to 89.5°, but by now a 'bingo' fuel state dictated a return to base.

On return to Montreal most of the goals of the flights had been achieved, and a leisurely flight to Whitehorse, Yukon, was under-taken with a view to returning from there non-stop to Shawbury, whilst also refining the position of the Magnetic Pole. take-off on this last leg was shortly after 1000 on 25 May. The Magnetic Pole lay to the south of track and measurements confirmed that it was close to the Astronomer Royal's predicted position, 300 miles NNW of the Boothia Peninsula. The flight was uneventful but confirmed the hopeless inaccuracy of charted magnetic data throughout the whole polar area and of height data for Greenland. *Aries* landed at Shawbury at 1245 on 26 May 1945, having made the first non-stop flight from the North American Pacific coast to NW Europe in 18hrs. 26min. – about half the time taken by multi-hop lower-latitude brethren. A large contingent of VIPs and press witnessed the arrival, hosted by the Commandant, Air Cdr Mackworth and his Deputy, Gp Capt Richardson.

Since departing on 10 May 1945, *Aries* had flown over 24,000 miles in 110 hours. Amongst data recorded were 30,000 magnetic recordings and 2,000 photographs. Conditions had been harsh when compared with the shirt-sleeved flying environment of today. The captain explained that the 11 crew had endured the space of a then-typical railway compartment in which 19 hours were often spent in 60 degrees of frost, whilst also encumbered with oxygen masks. The doctor observed that sleepiness was not a predominant sign of fatigue within the crew – on the flight to the Geographical Pole many of them were awake for 56 hours yet remained unusually wakeful.

The flights were well reported in the national press and Wg Cdr McKinley presented the preliminary results to the Royal Geographical Society in December 1945. Likewise, Wg Cdr Maclure presented the technical aspects to both the RGS and the American Institute of Navigation (at this time the British equivalent had yet to be formed); medical details were also presented. The three wing commanders were awarded the AFC and all other crew members were also decorated. David McKinley achieved the rank of AVM; in 1995 he was granted Honorary membership of the Royal Institute of Navigation (RIN) at a ceremony to celebrate the 50th anniversary of the polar flight. Flt Lt Underwood retired as a Wg Cdr and also survives, but sadly neither Andy Anderson nor Ken Maclure do so; they became respectively President and Vice-President of the RIN, which holds an Anderson Memorial Lecture annually.

Aries itself was involved in many further demonstration and research flights, often leading to records. These included London-Cape Town in 32hrs. 21min. in June 1946 and, in August 1946, London-Karachi-Darwin and -Wellington; the latter's time of 59hrs. 51min. almost halved the previous 104hrs. 20min. set in 1938 by Clouston and Ricketts in a Comet. *Aries* was finally retired in January 1947. It was earmarked for preservation and put into long-term storage, but sadly the order was rescinded and the aircraft was sold for scrap in August 1948. But the *Aries* sign from the nose was preserved and is now displayed in the *Aries* Club at RAF Shawbury, where a tree dedicated to the memory of *Aries* still thrives and where one station aircraft always carries the *Aries* name.

ARIES II

Aries was replaced by a Lincoln Mk 2, RE364, in December 1946 and, since the *Aries* name was to be retained, the aircraft was christened *Aries II* in February 1947. It was delivered to the Avro factory at Langar where, as with its predecessor, all armour and turrets were removed, Lancastrian-type nose and tail fairings fitted and the skin polished; indeed RE364 became known as a 'Lincolnian'. Extra tankage took the fuel up to 4,600 gallons and this time crew comfort was considered, with the rear of the aircraft lagged, heated and fitted with six seats and a bunk and cooking facilities. The oxygen supply was also boosted to cope with 12 crew at 20,000ft. for 24 hours. An extensive navigation fit included an API Mk II, GPI Mk II and G3 compass as well as the 'special' gyro from *Aries I*.

Aries II was never used for Arctic flying but it did fly with the Spec N Courses to the Far East, South Africa (breaking the London-Cape Town record at 26hrs. 57min. with Wg Cdr G F Rodney as captain), North America, Australia and New Zealand. The latter flight involved an extensive assessment of magnetic variation, for which 12 compasses were carried. The aircraft was, however, a disappointment in that it never met its range expectations. It was also short-lived, as in January 1948 a refuelling fire at Shawbury prior to departure for the Far East caused extensive damage, and the aircraft was written-off.

ARIES III

This could have spelt the end of the *Aries* line, but no – by late 1948 an 'extremely annoyed' Air Council agreed to a replacement and Avro were asked to convert another Lincoln, RE367, at Langar. The conversion of *Aries III* was to be similar to that of its predecessor; indeed, the nose fairing had been salvaged from the refuelling fire. A notable omission, however, was that of the crew-comfort features. The conversion was made in great haste, and when the aircraft was handed over in October 1948 it still carried the standard bomber colour scheme, with *Aries* appearing in white on the nose. The next two years saw plenty of routine, but not spectacular flying, although *Aries* was loaned to the Empire Flying School in April 1949 for assessing the new Calvert runway approach lighting at Heathrow. In July 1949 the aircraft formally moved to Manby, where the RAF Flying College had formed as an amalgamation of the 'Empire' schools. By late 1950 *Aries III* boasted a polished metal and white finish and the code FGAW.

In October 1950 *Aries III* set off from Strubby and overflew Heathrow to claim a new London-Khartoum record of 14hrs 23min. Shortly afterwards it made an easterly circumnavigation under the captaincy of Sqn Ldr Downey; the UK-Australia sector took 62 hours and after an extensive tour of RAAF bases the aircraft returned via Fiji, Hawaii, USA and Bermuda. July 1951 saw a return to the North Geographical Pole under the command of Wg Cdr Frogley, with Wg Cdr Humphrey (later to become Air Chief Marshal) as co-pilot and Flt Lt Grocott (who retired in the rank of Air Cdr and is currently RIN President) as one of the navigators. The techniques and conditions were similar to those of the first such flight. High-latitude fixing was to be based on a 20-minute sun-moon cycle, but the flight out of Keflavik saw cloud and icing problems as before, with aircraft height being varied between 11,000ft. and 20,000ft. in an attempt to ameliorate the effects. Nevertheless, the Pole was reached and *Aries III* flew on to Eielson USAF base in Alaska. The return was also similar to the 1945 flight, passing within 180 miles of the refined position of the Magnetic Pole, crossing the west Greenland coast near Thule and landing at Manby after a non-stop 19hrs. 34min.

An interesting visit was made to Ascension Island in September 1951. The aircraft refuelled at Accra and had to carry enough fuel for the return trip to Accra; Ascension was practically derelict and *Aries III* was only the second aircraft to visit since 1945. A trip to the Far East took place in January 1952 under the captaincy of Sqn Ldr Oakley. This was to Japan via Bahrain and Singapore and it is interesting to note the crew duty times involved – 18.5 hours for each of the first two legs, with a stop-over in Bahrain of just 4.5 hours! *Aries III's* last flight of note was back to the North Geographical Pole in September 1952, under the command of Sqn Ldr Lawrence. The route was again via Keflavik with the intention of flying on from the Pole to Whitehorse, Yukon, but shortly after leaving 90°N a fuel problem enforced a diversion to Thule, where the aircraft was stuck for two weeks. It ultimately returned to Manby in company with the Hastings that had ferried out the repair team. A final flight to Singapore was made in January 1953, but by this time Lincolns were being withdrawn from service and in September 1953 *Aries III* suffered the same fate.

ARIES IV

By now the Canberra had arrived on the scene and the Flying College was successful in bidding for one as *Aries IV;* this was to be a new pale-blue B2, WH699, which arrived at Manby in the spring of 1953. It was fitted with a 650-gallon bomb-bay fuel tank and navigation kit ultimately included an AMI, Mk II periscope sextant, a suspension bracket for a Mk IX stand-by sextant, Rebecca, radio-compass and improved communication radios.

Aries IV's first notable flight was in celebration of the 50th anniversary of the Wright brothers' first powered flight. Return London-Cape Town trips, each of 6,010 miles, in December 1953 set records both ways: outbound in 12hrs. 21min., less than half *Aries II's* time, with Wg Cdr Petty and Sqn Ldrs MacGarry and McDonald-Craig; and inbound in 13hrs. 16min. with Wg Cdr Humphrey and Sqn Ldrs Bower and Powell. March 1954 also saw a record of 6hrs 15min for a flight from Montreal to Manby.

But a more spectacular accomplishment took place in October 1954, when *Aries IV* made the first British jet flight to the North Geographical Pole (not a world first – a USAF B-52 had reached the Pole in the spring of 1952); it was to be a training and technique-proving exercise. Wg Cdr Humphrey was pilot once more, with Sqn Ldr Bower and Flt Lt Wood navigating. After a series of previous practice runs it had been decided to make the flight from Bardufoss, with Bödo as terminal and Thule as en route diversions. Astro was to be the primary navigation aid and this dictated a night-time sortie, using the periscopic sextant to determine both position lines and heading checks. The standard gyro-magnetic compass was put into gyro above 78°N, with half-hourly heading and position-line checks and an hourly cycle of full fixes. Fuel was so critical that the aircraft was towed to the runway prior to take-off and the sortie flown in the most efficient cruise-climb possible, starting at 42,500ft. The flight was successful, with the Pole overflown at 2313Z on 14 October 1954, although with OAT down to -65°C life became extremely cold for crew and equipment; the radio-compass and Rebecca packed up altogether, the VHF almost so and the sextant mounting became extremely stiff. Moreover, an unwelcome weather diversion to Bödo became necessary on return; the flight had lasted 6hrs. 43min.

Aries IV's final record-breaking foray took place in June 1955, when it was flown from Bardufoss to Fairbanks via the Pole in 6hrs

30min. and then Wg Cdr Broom, with Sqn Ldrs Bower and Seymour, flew from Ottawa to London in 6hrs 42min. – a new record representing an average speed of 431 knots. Although it was ousted by *Aries V* the following year, *Aries IV* remained active with the Flying College until it was written off in a take-off accident at Strubby in November 1959.

Aries IV has not been forgotten, however, and another Canberra B2 (actually WJ637) had been turned into a replica of WH699, resplendent in blue and with the records faithfully reproduced on the nose. It stands outside Cranwell's Trenchard Hall, home of the GD Aerosystems Course.

ARIES V

Canberras had progressed since the B2, and a PR7 – WT528 – joined the College's fleet at Manby in June 1956. Painted silver, with red tailplane, fin and wingtips, it carried a similar navigation fit to its predecessor, but very much more fuel – over 4,000 gallons. The aircraft had already achieved two records in the hands of an English Electric crew in August 1955 – London-New York and return in a total of 17hrs 42min, including a 35-minute turn-round in USA; it was the first such round-trip in a single day.

Aries V's only claim in the record books was that of time between Tokyo and London (actually West Malling) in May 1957. Wg Cdr Hoy and Flt Lts Lageson and Denis made the trip, via Alaska and the North Atlantic, in 17hrs 44min. But setting records was not the primary task of the Flying College, and in April 1958 *Aries V,* with some logistical help from *Aries IV,* undertook an easterly round-the-world trip to develop navigational techniques for areas with limited navigation aids on the ground, and to discuss operations and training with Commonwealth air forces. The first leg, to Nairobi in 8hrs 12min, was substantially the fastest ever, but was not claimed as a record; the tour went on to cover South Africa, Australia and New Zealand.

Aries V carried on into the early 1960s, but was ultimately converted at Warton into a PR57 for the Indian Air Force. Indeed, by 1966, all Canberras had been withdrawn from Manby, which had become the College of Air Warfare in 1962.

END OF AN ERA

This not only represented the end of the line for dedicated *Aries* aircraft, but also the end of a post-war era during which a centre of expertise had been established, and given the wherewithal, to develop and disseminate navigation techniques. *Aries V's* round-the-world trip in 1958 had very similar aims to that of *Aries I's* in 1945; record-breaking and 'showing the flag' were pleasant secondary effects. But a combination of reduced funding and escalating technology put an end to these activities in this form, although navigational expertise and *Aries*-style flights would remain essential.

OTHER POLAR FLYING

It should not be forgotten that during the period 1945 to 1960 *Aries* aircraft were not the only ones to venture to very high latitudes, and even to the Geographical Pole itself. Virtually all such flights were conducted by way of Spec N training, which regularly involved long lower-latitude flights as well – the Spec N courses of the late '40s and early '50s all seemed to have an attraction for Khartoum!

No 9 Spec N detached to Keflavik in March 1951 with five Lancasters; they conducted training flights to Jan Mayen and the east Greenland coast. The September 1952 flight of *Aries III* to the Geographical Pole was a component of a detachment involving a Lincoln and two Hastings. The former was to cover a triangular route to Churchill (Manitoba) and Goose Bay, with the Hastings flying to Resolute Bay, close to the Magnetic Pole. Sun-moon fixes were still the order of the day and planning was achieved using the Greenaway Twilight Computer, modified to show the availability of such fixing. Gyro steering and the use of the Greenwich grid were also the norm. Interestingly, the main observations from this detachment were the need for a positive fixing aid other than astro, and for reliable meteorological information.

No 13 Spec N detached to Resolute Bay with two Hastings in May 1955, and at least one reached 90°N. And June 1956 saw No 14 Spec N detach to Bödo with four Lincolns for polar flying. At least one of them might have made the Geographical Pole had communications been good enough to have permitted reduced fuel reserves; as it was it made 88° 37'N. Navigation techniques were similar to those of previous sorties, using astro and gyro-steering, although other aids such as pressure-pattern and H2S were also tried.

A NEW ERA

As we have seen, long-range and high-latitude flying had been an integral part of Spec N training, but with the demise of the *Aries* aircraft at the end of the '50s, the name *Aries* was adopted as the name of a series of flights, not aircraft. By now the aim of the flights had also changed from the development of navigation techniques to the testing of navigation equipment. The adoption of larger aircraft enabled representatives from industry to join the flights, bringing with them their latest equipment, often in prototype form. Members of the OR Branches could also see 'their' equipment in action.

This era started in 1960, when Britannias were adopted for the *Aries* flights. Typically they could accommodate a trials crew of 50, with Manby installing the trials tables and equipment. A typical trip would be direct to Thule on the first day, with the second seeing a longer trip up to the Pole and thence direct to Brize Norton. The 20-hour round trip would be flown twice within a week to accommodate the usual 24 students and entourage. Students were no longer responsible for the navigation of the aircraft, but the back of the Britannia would be a sea of flickering displays, slide-rules and charts.

RAF Britannias were withdrawn from service in 1974, but A&AEE Boscombe Down retained one, and this was made available for the *Aries* trips. Installation was easier, as more time could be allocated to producing a shaken-down system, and much expertise was on hand. This situation lasted until 1983, when the demise of this last Britannia saw a return to Brize Norton and the adoption of the VC-10 in 1984. This proved to be spacious and comfortable, the only real snag being its speed; much of the benefit of the trips was derived from students moving between equipment and experts, and the '10s round-trip time was considerably shorter than its predecessors'.

On approaching the current decade, the acquisition of a VC-10 each year became ever more problematical and in 1990 it was decided to accept the offer to move back to A&AEE to use the trials Comet 4C, XS235 *'Canopus'*. This had the disadvantages of being much smaller than the VC-10 and of not possessing the range, but it could boast the considerable advantage of having an innate datum and recording system of world-class. At first the Comet flights were routed to Cyprus through weather and range constraints, but more recently they have made Thule and the Geographic Pole. It should be mentioned that not all post-1960 *Aries* flights have followed the Thule-North Pole route; the 1984 trip, for instance, was very similar to that of *Aries I*, taking in both Geographical and Magnetic Poles.

And, mentioning anomalies, it should be noted that one *Aries* flight to Cyprus was conducted in a Hercules!

So how does a recent *Aries* trip compare with its predecessor of 50 years ago? Of course we now have a warm, quiet environment, but putting that aside, the objectives are almost identical except that emphasis is made on equipment performance rather than navigation technique: 'investigate polar transit performance'; 'investigate high-latitude align capability'; and 'observe ionospheric effects on GPS at high latitudes'. Trials equipment carried on a typical mid-'90s flight included seven GPS installations, one INS, two integrated INS/GPS and two flight management systems. The post-flight differential GPS datum was available on floppy disc at 5-second intervals and to an accuracy of better than 2 metres!

END OF THE LINE?

The *Aries* flights have been in good hands for over 50 years and the aircraft that have been involved are nicely portrayed on the postal cover commemorating the 50th anniversary of *Aries I's* polar achievement. They have represented the forefront of the development of navigation techniques and equipment, and could continue to do so, given the opportunity. Directly and indirectly, they have certainly made a profound contribution to both military and civil aircraft navigation. But the present vehicle for the flights, Comet XS235, is due to be retired in 1997, and we wait in some trepidation for a possible successor to emerge.

Whatever the future, we should remember *Aries* with pride, and if one were to pluck out a couple of events in particular they would surely be the two 'firsts' – *Aries I* over the North Pole on 17 May 1945, and *Aries IV* likewise on 14 October 1954.

Aries I in 1944 before its 'Lancastrian' conversion

Aries I, modified for polar flights, at Keflavic in May 1945

The crew of Aries I on completion of the flight to the Geographical Pole, May 1945

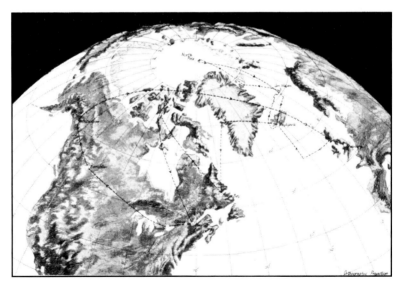

The routes flown by Aries I

Aries II, the Lincoln RE364, resplendent in natural metal finish

The Aries III crew on arrival at Manby from the polar flight, August 1951

Typical north polar ice, taken from Aries III in 1951

*Aries V (on right) christened at Manby in June 1955, with its older
brother Aries IV (on left)*

A&AEE's Britannia hosted the Aries flights during the late 70's and early 80's

Since 1990 Boscombe Down's Comet 4C, 'Canopus', has been the main host of the Aries flights; but is due for disposal in 1997

A typical recent Aries scene – the laboratory area of Comet XS235 in the mid-1990's

Not forgotten. Part of the nose of Aries I being presented to RAF Shawbury, in October 1984 by AVM David McKinley: Gp Capt Dickie Richardson is on the left. 'Canopus' is in the background

9. Developments in the Early 1950s

Air Vice-Marshal Jack Furner

Chairman's Introduction

To describe the developments in the early 50's Air Vice-Marshal Jack Furner is going to talk to us now. He served for 35 years in the RAF, during which time he flew 42 types of aircraft with 243 different pilots. I think that a special medal should be struck for such bravery. Jack did two tours in Bomber Command in World War 2 before joining Transport Command in the Far East; and after the War he served at Boscombe and at Dayton, Ohio; commanded Scampton with three Vulcan 'Blue Steel' squadrons, and his last post was as the Assistant Air Secretary. In the 70's he was Chairman of the Aries Association . . . Jack . . .

My part in these proceedings is something of an interlude – an interlude between on the one hand, the hectic and dangerous days and nights of World War II and on the other the exciting prospect to come of the introduction of the V-Force with its awesome banks of navigational and bombing systems.

So – we are in the early 1950s. And we are at Boscombe Down in Wiltshire and Wright Patterson in Dayton, Ohio. Those were the days, many of you will recall, of countless new jets appearing at the annual Farnborough airshows and the Mayor of Farnborough signalling "Bang On!" to sonic booms despite local protests; the days of test bed aircraft like the flying bedstead, the forerunner of the Harrier and, at Boscombe Down, the Ashton (an early British 4-jet) being used to carry out flight trials of new equipment and new techniques; the days of miniature Vulcans in formation with their bigger brother and the days when, for instance, the Victor would stagger round the Boscombe circuit on its first test run and Sir Fred would announce that it had flown higher, faster and further than any jet before it, and in our context today, the days of intriguing new navigation and bombing equipments being developed at RRE and RAE: Dopplers, new and significantly advanced marks of H2S, inertials with their doubleintegration from acceleration to distance, and the birth of the technique of picture matching – flogging across the Sahara at night in a Lincoln following the radar pictures of an earlier flight – little did we know how that technique might be used decades later. And across the pond at USAF airfields like Wright Patterson and Edwards, the same thing only times about a dozen and at vastly greater expense, the nav/bombing systems of the B-47, the B-52, and the enormous B-36 (with "6 turnin' and 4 burnin' ") and future development work particularly in the field of inertials – IBM and Sperry and a host of others producing inertial gymbals over 5 feet across. Those were early days for inertials: they would in due course be much miniaturised.

But what I should like to do now in my short time up here is to zero in, as just one example, on a series of flight trials designed to evaluate one particular new piece of equipment – the RAF's first Doppler system. Remember Christian Doppler? An Austrian, who in 1842 was the first to discover the effect of velocity on observed frequencies of light and sound. He tested his theory out on a train load of trumpeters. We sense the Doppler effect in sound all around us in any city, from police vehicles and ambulances.

Well, in the summer of 1953 the Doppler equipment developed by RRE was delivered for trials at Boscombe Down on behalf of the then Ministry of Supply. It was called Green Satin – the Royal Navy's version was Blue Silk. Green Satin was installed for the trials in a Canberra.

What was Green Satin? Simply a drift and groundspeed meter. OR No 3015 specified for it in 1949 as follows:

Groundspeed 100-700 kts, accuracy <0.2%

Drift from 20 P to 20 S, accuracy <0.1 of a degree

Day or night, anywhere in the world

Over land or water, any time of year

Heights to 60,000 feet

Normal flight attitudes

All weathers

The Green Satin aerial was designed to seek out the maximum frequency shift between the signal out and the signal back, hence was aligned with track and could show the angle between its installed position and its track position – which of course equalled drift; and the measure of that maximum frequency shift gave us groundspeed. Add compass heading to the drift and you had track; take the track plus the distance travelled into a simple computer (then called the Ground Position Indicator Mark 4) and you had northing and easting or along and across track, according to choice.

As you saw from the OR, here was something of a completely new order of accuracy. I know the younger chaps present will smile at that statement when they think of their satellites and their Ground Position Systems measuring accuracy in feet, but this was hot stuff in the early 50s. And the problem to be faced was – what do we measure its accuracy against? What were to be our datum equipments?

We needed an accurate fixing device and an accurate heading. So what options were there? For fixing, three options: aerial photography (dismissed because of weather); ground radar fixing (dismissed because of decreasing accuracy with increasing distance from transmitter); and fixing in the air from the then hyperbolic lattices – Gee or Decca. Of the two, Decca was the more accurate and, just as important, lent itself much more conveniently to photographic recording. Hence Decca Mark 6 was chosen as the most accurate position datum available; and the best accuracy was to be found along the right bisector between the master transmitter and one of the slaves. 100 nm runs were plotted, one over land and one over sea, as the optimum lengths in accuracy terms. The 50% error at the extremities of those 100 nm runs was calculated to be in the order of 60 yards. Ordnance Survey prepared for us special Decca lattice charts on a scale of 1 inch = 1 kilometre. The displays of Green Satin, GPI4, G4B compass and Deccometers were all covered by an A4 camera in a specially designed housing.

As to a heading datum, the G4B compass itself was hopeless of course. Even with the comparatively sophisticated Fourier analysis applied to compass swinging, the remaining uncertainties of both deviation and magnetic variation made the compass a crude heading datum.

Therein lies the main problem with a device like Green Satin. To add its anticipated drift accuracy to that of the compass of those days was like adding champagne and ginger beer. Fortunately the problem had been foreseen a year or two previously by Farnborough; they had designed what they called an Azimuth Datum Instrument (ADI) for these very trials – a recording periscope bearing plate, from which aircraft's true heading would be determined by sun observations. The ADI was installed on the port side of the navigator's hatch in such a position that the projected display of the instrument was directly in front of his head. The image was photographed by a 35mm camera; it's interesting to recall that the installation invalidated the escape facility of the navigation hatch of the Canberra. The explosive bolts in the navigator's seat were therefore removed. In addition there was reason to doubt the reliability of the dome of the ADI under stress of cabin pressure: the Canberra was therefore flown unpressurised and unheated for the bulk of the flying.

After being satisfied that the installations were as perfect as they could be, that the Green Satin aerial was as accurately aligned with the fore and aft axis of the aircraft as possible, and that all necessary calculations were ready for analysis after flight, the flight trials began. There were 57 flights made in the Canberra; some over land, some over sea; some low, down to 300 feet; most at medium levels, around 30,000 feet; a few high, up to 52,500 feet; at groundspeeds from 100kts to 550kts; the lowest air temperature experienced was -61 degrees C; most flights, as I said, were flown unpressurised and unheated; all flights with no rear escape. The thick frost that formed over everything at height dripped nicely down on to the navigator as descent melted the frost.

On each run, photographic recordings of all instruments were made every 6 seconds. Readings of the films back on the ground were made to the nearest 0.1 degree for drift; 0.1 nm for distance; 0.01 of a Decca lane; 0.01 of a degree for sun's azimuth.

Inevitably in a trial of this kind there were a number of special factors which were significant in varying degrees and had to be taken into account in one way or another.

Alignment of the Green Satin aerial was, of course, vital. Any error in alignment would obviously translate into systematic drift error. Two alignment checks were made during the trials. Both were geometrical – not electronic. The alignment process involved the use of a theodolite and the projection of aircraft and aerial fore and aft axis on the ground. The accuracy of a single alignment observation was determined to be +/- 0.02 of a degree in terms of 50% error.

Then there was the Azimuth Datum Instrument, the ADI, to align. The aircraft's true heading determined by theodolite observations from a trigonometrical station was compared with apparent true heading deduced from the difference between calculated sun's azimuth and sun's relative bearing measures on the ADI.

Once in the air, there were a number of additional special factors:

There was clearly going to be a great difference between performances over land and over sea. For two reasons. Firstly, the question of signal strength. If the sea was smooth there would be insufficient return of signal to give any sensible results – in fact, it was found that below a 5kt surface wind, unlocking would almost certainly occur at normal heights. Secondly, the sea surface most often is moving, as a result of both surface wind and tide. The combined effect is to produce a vector error in the Green Satin results. For instance, movement in a reciprocal direction to aircraft's track would cause over-reading of groundspeed. Studies were made on all sea runs of the three vectors – tide and surface wind on the one hand and Green Satin error on the other – and broad correlation was noted.

Performance in turns depended on the rate of turn and the angle of bank. The higher in both cases, the more chance of unlocking. Similarly in pitch – when an aircraft with Green Satin climbs or dives, an error must be incurred in distance measurement. It must be said that it didn't behave very well with Bomber Command's World War II-type corkscrewing!

Next we have an unusual one – a factor not considered worth bothering about in any previous equipment. Green Satin's distance gone calculation assumed the nautical mile (that is, a minute of latitude) to be 6,080 feet in length and therefore gave correct distance information only at sea level at 48 degrees latitude. At height at that latitude it measured and registered a false ground distance: at 40,000 the error was 0.2% – 2 miles in a 1,000. This type of error was allowed for in our calculations. If you significantly changed latitude then a similar error was incurred: at the Equator the length of a minute of latitude is 6,045 feet. I stress that there was nothing new about these errors. They had always existed with such instruments as ASIs and APIs. The important point was that, for the first time, the value of these errors fell outside the accuracy limits of the new equipment.

On the ground, films were read every six seconds, averages taken over minute periods, and Green Satin error was a calculation of the difference between datum position –Decca fixing – and a position given by true heading from the ADI, Green Satin drift and Green Satin distance. Similar calculations were made in assessing the GPI4.

The subsequent document written for the Ministry of Supply submitted that the accidental errors of Green Satin over land in straight and level flight were less than +/- 0.1% of distance flown and less than +/- 0.1 of a degree in drift. Additional errors would be incurred due to aircraft height, change of latitude, sea movement, misalignment of the aerial array and changes of aircraft altitude. However, these errors taken together were small compared with the directional error of the aircraft's heading transmitted by the G4B compass into the GPI.

The message to the coming V-Force had to be – here is a valuable and accurate tool to be used in your nav/bombing systems, but the desperate need, as ever over so many decades, is for equally accurate heading. Whatever your heading system, compass swings will be of critical importance.

10. From the 60s to the 80s "The Last Days of Airborne Analogue Computing"

Air Commodore Norman Bonnor

Chairman's Introduction

To cover the 60's to the 80's we have Air Commodore Norman Bonnor to talk to us. After two operational tours on Victors the bulk of Norman's 33 years in the RAF was spent on research and development, including Phantom Avionics and Nimrod Mk2 Refit. He commanded RAF Waddington, after which he was Deputy Director of Operational Requirements at the MOD. After leaving the RAF in 1990 he joined GEC Marconi Electronic Systems Corporation. He currently runs a post-graduate course on Navigation Technology at Nottingham University . . . Norman . . .

The Valiant, Victor and Vulcan aircraft entered service in the late 50s, each equipped with a True Airspeed Unit, Green Satin, a Ground Position Indicator Mk4, the Navigation and Bombing System (NBS) which included H2S Mk IXA, a radar altimeter, a periscopic sextant but their only heading reference was a single G4B gyro-magnetic compass. These were the navigation aids for use in the aircrafts' war role of strategic bombing. To meet peacetime requirements, particularly for standard instrument departure and arrival procedures, other navigation equipment included: GEE Mk3, two radio compasses, ILS and later TACAN; I don't intend dealing with the use of these aids except to say that we also used the radio compasses for reception of Consol and to keep in touch with Test Match scores.

The major innovation when compared to earlier bomber aircraft was the real time input of accurate drift and groundspeed into the computations of a fully integrated navigation and bombing system. NBS was a very complex analogue computer. Among its many features were the calculation of forward throw and trail of a selected weapon and the output of accurate steering commands to the release point; unfortunately, it was large and very heavy involving many "black boxes", or perhaps these are better described as "black dustbins".

Green Satin was very reliable in squadron use and, apart from unlocking problems over calm seas and the inherent errors caused by surface motion, easily met the performance requirements of strategic bombing. The same could not be said of the G4B compass. A great deal of effort was devoted to ground compass swings using Fourier analysis to confirm the quality of the results, but large cross track errors were still very obvious in the air despite the use of an automatic variation unit which continuously applied the local variation value to the compass output. But before I delve more deeply into the compass errors, I should briefly describe the navigation team and techniques we used in those early days of the V Force.

The Nav Team comprised a Nav Radar, who had undergone a ten month training course at the Bombing School at Lindholme on radar scope interpretation and the detailed operation of the NBS system, and the Plotter who, in those early days, had completed at least one previous flying tour with above average assessments. To navigate to the target area, the Plotter used a traditional flight plan proforma, a separate navigation log and usually a Lamberts Conformal chart. The Nav Radar used 1:250,000 topographical maps to select suitable radar fix points for the en-route phase and large scale maps and aerial photographs to study the target area and to select offset aiming points for the target which usually was not an individual return on the radar. The offset distances were measured or calculated as accurately as possible in yards and set on the NBS as Northings and Eastings. Here is the second reason why compass errors were so important to the Nav Team; these offsets were against a true North datum, so any error in the true heading used by the NBS appeared directly in the bombing results. For example, using an offset 10,000 yards from target (not a particularly long one) a degree of heading error would introduce more than 150 yards bombing error over and above any aiming, ballistics or other errors.

Bomber Command imposed three navigation modes or techniques on the Nav Team for combat readiness training: Primary, Secondary and Limited. Primary allowed full use of all aids including radar fixing which made staying within about a ¼ mile of track and timing to better than 5 seconds very easy. Secondary assumed loss of the radar picture for fixing but Green Satin inputs were still available.

This meant using other methods for updating present position with the emphasis on Astro as the war role demanded autonomy. For navigators from an earlier era, I should point out that visual "on-tops" are not usually available or very accurate from 50,000 feet.

The V Force took Astro techniques to their limit; the old three star fix was largely abandoned in favour of along and across track position lines formed from averaging at least five one minute sextant runs (in effect 300 individual measurements) with complex corrections applied for turning and longitudinal acceleration errors. A good crew achieved errors of 3 to 5 miles at the terminal point of a 1,000 mile state using Secondary technique.

Limited technique took away the Green Satin inputs, leaving the True Airspeed feed and wind vectors set manually on the NBS. This was clearly more difficult, but if the high level winds were reasonably stable, a good crew would be inside 10 miles at the end of 1,000. Almost all the Plotters I flew with used track plots for all three techniques including Limited where fixes or MPPs were used to calculate "delta" values of the N/S and E/W wind vectors to update the NBS settings. Height finding, very important for bombing, was conducted over the sea or over flat terrain of known height, using the Radar Altimeter to update the millibar setting on the barometric altimeter sub-system within the NBS.

But back to our real problem, the gyro-magnetic compass. The crews knew it was the weak link which is why so much attention was paid to the reducing residual deviations by elaborate compass swings. However, at squadron level, not much was known or understood about hang-off compass errors caused by flying rhumb line headings at 500 knots. On XV Squadron, we elected to air swing the compasses of all our Victor aircraft using Astro as the reference. To do this with sufficient accuracy, we fitted "Vernier" scales to the sextant azimuth rings and calculated the sun's azimuth to 0.1 of a degree by inter-polating the values in the yellow band AP3270. To our amazement, all eight of the squadron aircraft showed a very similar pattern of errors, with residual deviations of almost two degrees on SW headings. Later, when I left the squadron to complete the Staff and Specialist Navigation courses, I learned how to calculate these errors. Back on the squadron, we started using the airswing deviations, and our navigation performance and bombing results immediately improved. We also developed and used another technique to reduce the effect of compass errors on our bombing. This involved making the initial line up on the target with an abeam offset so that any compass errors were manifested along track as range errors; in the late stages of the run (10 or 15 seconds to release) the Nav Radar would tell the pilot to ignore the steering command and freeze on heading; he then switched to an offset in the overshoot and took out the range errors on this new offset.

Having solved the heading problem for high level navigation and bombing, the Soviets intervened by increasing their deployment of surface-to-air missiles. For some time, we had trained to defeat the SA1 and SA2 systems deployed around Moscow, and other major targets, by jamming their fire control radars and by weaving our heading throughout the bombing run so that their prediction systems could not track for long enough to achieve a successful engagement. But in 1963, the SA3 was deployed in large numbers with almost complete coverage along the Soviet border and in depth around our planned targets or Accounting Line numbers (ALNs) as they were known. To maintain the credibility of deterrence, tactics had to change; it was time to go low level to penetrate under the surveillance radar cover and below the effective height of the SA3 system; in reality, this meant not more than 500 feet and lower over the tops of ridges and hills.

Low level navigation was new to most of us. At high level, the pilots had flown on instruments with covers fitted over the cockpit windows to shield their eyes from the flash effects of other nuclear bursts; now the forward covers were removed, and the pilots issued with an eye patch so that at least two eyes out of four would still be available after flying close to someone else's ALN. The low level navigation technique we developed involved the Plotter giving a running commentary of the scene ahead from prepared ½ million topos which the pilots confirmed whenever they were in visual contact. Meanwhile, the Nav Radar used terrain features in preference to cultural fix points to check and update the NBS position at regular intervals. Terrain screening on the radar picture was very pronounced below 500 feet, and the important characteristic for a feature to show changed from what it was made of – metal or brick – to how high it was. Often a field pattern created by stone walls or hedges, or railway embankments, were much more prominent features than towns or industrial areas.

In the early 60s, some of the Valiant aircraft went out of service as bombers and were converted to the tanker role, and the Mk 2 versions of the Vulcan and Victor entered service. Apart from later versions of Green Satin and NBS, the initial navigation fit of the Mk 2s was the same as the Mk 1s except for the compass. The G4B was replaced by twin gyro-magnetic compasses incorporated as part of the Smiths Military Flight System: unfortunately, these suffered from very similar errors to the G4B but did have the added advantage that the pilots could now select to fly heading or track on a true or magnetic datum.

The next change came with the introduction of the Blue Steel missile which gave a stand-off range of 150 miles at 60,000 feet or 50 miles at low level; with it came the GPI Mk 6, probably the most accurate analogue aircraft computer ever built, and the inertial navigation system of the missile itself. The aircraft would use the outprints of this system until the missile was launched. At last, an accurate source of true heading once the IN was aligned, but here was the rub; the V Force role involved rapid reaction from the famous 4-minute warning, hence no time for a 15 to 20 minute ground alignment. Airborne alignments had to be used; remember, this was long before GPS and the very rapid in-motion alignments we now take for granted.

After a scramble take-off, which the first aircraft using a simultaneous start of all four engines could achieve within 50 seconds, the gimballed gyro platform of the Blue Steel IN was initially caged to the aircraft's axes and the best estimate of true heading. Once the gyros were at full speed and their temperature stabilised, the physical caging was released and Doppler/IN mixing commenced. In level flight, the inertial velocities N/S and E/W were effectively slaved to the resolved Doppler values by torquing the IN platform. With the platform levelled, the next step was to improve its heading accuracy; this was achieved by assuming that any cross track error between successive radar fixes was the result of azimuth misalignment. For this to be a reasonable assumption, the fixes were taken about 20 minutes apart and heading changes between them were limited to no more than 30 degrees. This rather lengthy alignment technique was completed by the Nav Team using the GPI Mk6, the NBS and the Blue Steel Monitor Panel in what can only be called a "mandraulic" manner, i.e. each step was separately initiated, carefully monitored and required a number of switch selections; very different to the automated alignment sequence of modern Ring Laser Gyro Inertial Reference Systems. That said, the system worked well and achieved excellent navigation results.

In training, missile guidance accuracy was assessed by allowing the IN system to run free while the aircraft performed a manoeuvre designed to emulate the same effects on IN performance as the missile's Mach 3 flight profile would impose after launch; the results of this procedure were tested by a series of four missile firings in the Aberporth Bay range. By this stage, the Victor Mk 2 had been fitted with side-scan radar capability and a Rapid Processing Display Unit. When in use, the H2S scanner was locked at 90 degrees to aircraft track (port or starboard) and radar video diverted from the normal PPI display to a low afterglow CRT across which photographic paper was drawn at a speed proportional to the groundspeed of the aircraft. The exposed image was developed by passing the paper over two slots through which developing and fixing chemicals were sucked. Although it sounds hazardous to employ hot and corrosive chemicals in a pressurised aircraft cabin, the system was successful in that the radar image produced was much sharper and with a much wider spectral range than the normal high afterglow PPI; of course, it also produced a permanent image which allowed the Nav Radar to study the returns more carefully before making any updates. The RPU was only fitted to the Victor; I believe this small scale introduction was really aimed at developing the technique for the ill-fated TSR2 in which an RPU based side-scan radar was the primary fixing aid.

Meanwhile, the remaining Vulcan Mk 2 aircraft, not equipped with Blue Steel, were designated to be Skybolt carriers, and these were fitted with a new Heading Reference System (HRS) based on a twin gyro platform. Like the Blue Steel IN system, it had to be aligned in the air, but this time one of the techniques used was based on the method described earlier of using radar offsets to measure and correct its azimuth misalignment.

While this was the V Force experience through the 60s, the strategic transport force also received new aircraft and navigation equipment with 10 Belfasts and 14 VC10s in 1966 followed shortly afterwards by the Hercules. All three types relied on Doppler drift and groundspeed combined with gyro-magnetic compass heading to calculate a dead reckoning solution in an analogue GPI. For long range oceanic flights, astro fixing was supplemented by the Decca ADL 21, LORAN C. Some skill was required to operate this semi-automatic system well, but LORAN C was a very significant advance of LORAN A having much longer range and precision accuracy. Again the weak link in these aircraft was the heading reference. The VC10 navigators faced a major decision whenever they got airborne; which of the two Bendix Polar Path compasses to select as the main reference for the rest of the flight because a two degree heading difference always appeared just after take-off.

For Great Circle tracks on the long oceanic routes, grid techniques were employed using grivation on the gyro-magnetic reference but occasionally using free gyro steering as the newer gyros were pretty stable and local earth rate could now be corrected by a simple selection on the compass control panel. The VC10 and Belfast used the GPI Mk7 which incorporated some of the technology from the V Force GPI 6 but was very expensive for the accuracy it achieved.

In the early 70s, the first hybrid analogue/digital navigation system was developed for the new maritime patrol aircraft – the Nimrod. This system used the Elliott E3 inertial platform and Blue Silk Doppler, which was similar to Green Satin but with modified parameters for better operation over the sea. From the outset it was recognised that Doppler/Inertial velocity mixing would be essential to maintain the E3 platform in a local earth vertical reference frame over the long sorties required for maritime patrol, but how could the IN azimuth be aligned for the best accuracy? Clearly the V Force fix monitored azimuth technique would not be available on sorties from coastal airfields. The method chosen was runway alignment, which involved the navigator setting a surveyed true heading of the runway into the IN controller, and the pilot positioning the aircraft on the centreline at brakes off and again just before lift off; the system used the inertial velocities during the take-off roll to determine any azimuth misalignment when compared with the surveyed heading and precessed the platform azimuth to correct for it.

All the sensors in the Mk I Nimrod were analogue, but the navigation calculations were performed in a digital computer – the 920B. Navigation performance was well beyond anything experienced in the old Shackleton, but didn't keep pace with the accuracy required for the role and the system was almost totally replaced during the Mk 2 refit programme in the early 80s, when a derivative of the Tornado IN system was installed together with a much more powerful computer.

Another hybrid analogue/digital system was in the final stages of development in the early 70s for use in the Harrier and Phantom. The 4 most complex LRUs were common to both aircraft, or were meant to be, but the escalating cost of maintaining commonality eventually outweighed any savings. The Harrier system included the first projected map display which was very popular with the pilots who had mostly come from no more than a map and stop watch in Hunters, but the Phantom fit was very much an afterthought to increase the British content of a mainly U.S. programme; so much so that the display panel readouts had to be modified with prisms so that the navigator could see them in his normal seat position. The core of the system was the Ferranti Miniature Platform designed to meet the accuracy required for these offensive support aircraft in a pure inertial mode. But this accuracy could only be achieved after a long ground alignment (15-20 minutes), and was significantly degraded if rapid align was used; there was no airborne alignment capability. These were the last of the IN systems designed in UK using analogue sensors.

The next generation, the E3R platform used in the Jaguar NAVWAS (Navigation and Weapon Aiming System) was fully digital. While this system was more reliable, the ergonomics of its installation in the Jaguar cockpit were far from ideal, and a number of unexplained accidents at low level were later attributed to the pilot being distracted when he went heads-down to make system selections.

At the end of the 70s, Omega became operational – the first truly global radio navigation system. MOD selected the Litton 211 system for the VC10, Hercules and Nimrod. This system gave excellent service and was subsequently fitted to a number of other aircraft for the Falklands War including the Victor Tankers, Vulcans and a Chinook. It also provided many crews with their first experience of automated route flying using a number of preset waypoints.

The next major development was for the Tornado which included the first digital platform designed by Ferranti, the FIN 1010. Mixing was reintroduced with Doppler and other sensors using the infamous Kalman Filter. Although the concept was not new (it was used on the Apollo missions and in the F-111) it required a great deal of development effort to achieve a workable computer model of the various sensors and to produce a practical filter design which did not become unstable in flight. The Tornado system also introduced the concept of "graceful degradation" of performance when one or more sensors failed.

The Tornado programme must be judged a success and an example of good "Top Down" design which sadly cannot be said of many other projects of the period. The Tornado also marked the RAF's first involvement with a "Glass Cockpit" albeit only for the navigator. The TV/Tab displays and their "Soft Keys" allowed a great deal of flexibility for the control and display of data in a limited cockpit space. Fortunately, the RAE team who developed the concept included experienced service aircrew who had a strong influence on the ergonomics of the design and prevented the scientists and engineers from introducing layer upon layer of nested keying sequences which would have been impractical in service use.

A further innovation of the Tornado is the ability to plan a flight in the crew room or operations centre and record it on an ordinary cassette tape. At crew in, the data is loaded into the aircraft system through the cockpit voice recorder initially. The route waypoints, targets and other details are then called up on the TV/Tabs and the sortie gets underway. This concept has spread to almost all the RAF's current front line aircraft which leads into the next paper, "The Present and the Future".

11. The Present and the Future – A Personal View

Air Commodore Bill Tyack

Chairman's Introduction

For out last talk this afternoon, and to bring us right up to date, we are pleased to have Air Commodore Bill Tyack. He is currently the Senior Military Officer in the Defence Evaluation and Research Agency. He has spent 34 years in the RAF, flying first in Shackletons and later commanding No. 51 (Nimrod) Squadron, and RAF Wyton. Bill has over 5,000 hours to his credit, and is currently the President of the Aries Association . . . Bill . . .

INTRODUCTION

When Professor Taylor wrote her classic history of navigation in the 1950s, she called it *"The Haven-Finding Art"*. And most navigators of my generation and older would agree that the navigation we were taught was an art, as well as a science. That is changing; over the last thirty years there have been enormous advances in the science of finding out precisely where you are on the surface of the earth. As this revolution has coincided almost exactly with my time as a navigator, I am very grateful for the opportunity to offer my perspective of navigation in the Royal Air Force at present and in the future. While I have had help in gathering facts from many people around the Service, for which I am very grateful, this is a personal view and does not represent Ministry of Defence policy.

I started my navigation career some 30 years ago in Shackleton maritime patrol aircraft. In those days, the Shackleton's radio navigation systems, such as ADF, Consol and Loran and the Doppler navigator, were not totally reliable for long range navigation; it was often very difficult or even impossible to detect the signals in noise and the coverage was by no means global. Once we were out of radar range of land – which was most of the time on Shackleton sorties – the only navigation aids which were totally dependable were watch, compass, drift sight and hand-held sextant. This basic equipment and the procedures were little different from those employed by Captain

Cook on his great voyages of discovery in the 18th Century. There was much art in Shackleton navigation and when we made a landfall error of only two or three miles after flying for ten or twelve hours using only drift sight and sextant we were quite proud of ourselves.

Now I can buy a hand-held satellite navigation system through a mail order catalogue for just over £200. The advertisements claim "Whether you are walking, climbing, fishing, cycling, driving, sailing or just plain lost, the amazing Global Positioning System gives you precise position to approximately 50 metres anywhere on the earth's surface. With its ultra compact size (similar to a mobile phone), ease of use and breakthrough price, the equipment literally puts satellite navigation into everyone's pocket!" What price the art of navigation now? Two hundred and fifty years ago John Harrison revolutionised maritime navigation by developing an accurate chronometer, which solved the critical problem of finding accurate longitude. I consider that the effect on aircraft navigation of the Global Positioning System (GPS) is just as revolutionary.

Thus advances in science and technology, epitomised by GPS, mean that the job of the aircraft navigator has changed, and continues to change. In fast-jet aircraft like the Tornado he, or she, is a weapon system operator. In some large aircraft like the Nimrod the navigator is a tactical director and mission commander. The job is much more than just navigation; it is "mission management", which I would define as: *all the activities involved in planning and conducting a mission to ensure that your own, or a co-operating platform's weapons arrive precisely on the right target at the right time.*

Mission management, therefore, is the topic of this paper. The potential scope of the paper is vast. However, space has forced me to be selective, and possibly arbitrary, in choosing themes and examples. Moreover it is impossible to make a neat division between the present and the future. This is, as the title explains, a personal view, but I believe it is representative.

The paper briefly describes the GPS system, as an example of current technology, then offers some examples of today's navigation systems, before outlining the current navigator training programme. Turning to the future, it looks again at technology and offers some examples of future systems. The navigation of weapons is mentioned and the paper concludes by speculating about future trends and raising the final question "Whither the Navigator".

THE PRESENT

Technology

GPS has had a revolutionary effect on position-finding in many applications, and this will continue because we have only just started to exploit its full potential. Its advent has already resulted in the demise of other long-range fixing systems, such as Loran and, soon Omega. The GPS system comprises 3 elements: the space segment; the equipment on the user vehicle; and a ground control segment. The space segment consists of a constellation of 24 satellites in semi-synchronous orbit at about 20,000 kilometres above the earth's surface. The orbits are arranged to ensure that 4 or more satellites, with a good geometry for fixing, will normally be observable at every location on earth. The principle is to measure the range from each of several satellites and then, knowing the position of the satellites, to calculate the position where the range arcs intersect. Each satellite has a very accurate clock and continuously transmits a ranging signal, which, in essence, is a very accurate timing signal. Superimposed is a navigation message containing precise orbital data for the satellite (its ephemerides) and other relevant information, such as ionospheric corrections. the system in the aircraft, which is completely passive, also has a very accurate clock; it receives the GPS transmissions and calculates the time delay and hence the range from each satellite. Then, using the transmitted satellite orbital data it establishes the aircraft's position. The range from 4 satellites will give position in 3 dimensions and also a correction to the aircraft's clock, which means that the receivers can use a much less accurate and hence cheaper clock than the satellites. This is one reason why commercial hand-held GPS sets can be bought so cheaply. The ground control segment contains a number of monitoring stations around the world, which receive the satellite transmissions and pass them to the master control station. The position of the monitoring stations is known precisely, so the master control can calculate any errors in satellite ephemirides and clock time. Corrections to these parameters are then uploaded to the satellites from ground antennas. The master control can also command a satellite to execute station-keeping manoeuvres if it is drifting away from the required orbit. The overall position accuracy obtainable from GPS is about 10 metres (one sigma) for the civil users and about 6 metres for military users, who can receive an encrypted signal. Importantly, this is a 3-dimensional position. This compares with about 400 metres for TACAN and 200 metres for DECCA or the TRANSIT satellite navigation system. GPS also provides velocity (again in three dimensions) to an accuracy of about one tenth of a metre per second.

A variant known as Differential GPS offers position accuracies of about 2 metres for terminal approaches to airfields. In this system, a very accurately-sited ground station, close to the touch-down point, receives GPS signals and retransmits them to the aircraft, where they are compared with the signals received directly by the aircraft, thus eliminating some of the systematic errors. In addition GPS can enable passive rendezvous, it is widely used for the guidance of weapons, and can be used for such applications as sonobuoy location. In this case, a simple, cheap receiver and transmitter on each sonobuoy can retransmit GPS signals to the aircraft where they are compared with directly received signals – in a similar manner to differential GPS. This provides very accurate knowledge of sonobuoy position, which in the anti-submarine warfare business is an important element of attack accuracy. There are countless other civil and military applications for GPS and the Royal Air Force has just started to exploit its full potential. Russia has developed a very similar satellite navigation system, working on the same principles, called GLONAS.

CURRENT NAVIGATION SYSTEMS

Table 1 shows a "typical" navigation fit for current large multi-engine aircraft in the RAF such as Nimrod, VC10 or Tristar, comprising: Gyro-magnetic compasses; a single or twin inertial navigation system; a stand-alone long-range fixing aid such as GPS, which the

Typical Multi-Engine Navigation Fit
■ Gyro-magnetic Compass
■ Inertial Navigation System
■ Long-range Fixing Aid
■ Weather Radar
■ Air Data System
■ VOR/DME/ILS
■ Dedicated Controls and Displays

Table 1

navigator can use to "fix" the inertial navigation position from time to time; a weather radar, which can also provide some ground mapping; an air data system; and VOR/DME/ILS for civil air traffic control and approach. Each equipment has individual controls and dedicated analogue or alphanumeric displays. Thus there is a full time job for the navigator to monitor all these systems and to integrate the information, while directing the aircraft on the optimum course for its mission, carrying out fuel calculations, talking on the radio to air traffic or checking on the latest weather at the destination or operating area.

The Nimrod MR2 is reasonably typical of the current generation of large military aircraft. The navigator's control panel contains controls and displays for; twin gyro-magnetic compasses; an inertial navigation system; a GPS; Omega; TACAN; VOR; Doppler navigator; and air data instruments. The controls and displays are not much different in appearance or principle from those of a Second World War Lancaster or Halifax. But one difference is that the Nimrod's digital computer takes in information from all these systems,aggregates it, gives steering signals to the autopilot, and displays navigation information such as position, velocity, wind velocity and ETAs on a TV-type display screen. This represents the beginning of the trend away from dedicated displays for each navigation sensor.

In contrast RAF Tristars have a civil airline fit of navigation equipment and the navigation is done by the pilots. It would be more correct to say that it is done by three inertial navigation systems under the control of a Digital Flight Management system, monitored by the pilots. The Flight Management System calculates the average

Typical Fast-Jet Navigation Fit

- Inertial Navigation System
- Moving Map Display
- Air-to-air Radar
- Air-to-ground Radar
- Terrain Following Radar
- Night Vision Goggles
- Forward-Looking Infra-Red
- Some General Purpose Displays and Controls

Table 2

position from two of the inertial navigators, leaving the third as a gross error check. It can steer the aircraft to its destination via the autopilot and autothrottle and can automatically tune the VOR and DME receivers to give the best fix, calculate the fix, then update the two inertial navigators to the fix position.

The typical fast-jet system is based on an inertial navigator. Table 2 lists the likely components such as: a moving map display, which projects the photographic image of a standard map onto a screen with aircraft and navigational data superimposed and the map moving in harmony with the aircraft's movement over the earth; an air-to-air radar or (depending on role) and air-to-ground radar, which provides ground mapping and targeting; a terrain following radar to enable fast, very low-level flight at night and in poor visibility, thereby to take advantage of terrain screening from hostile surface-to-air missiles and other defences; night vision goggles and, possibly, a forward-looking infra-red system to enable the crew to see to fly at low level and to identify and attack targets in the dark. The majority of information will be displayed on general purpose, TV-type display screens. For example in the Tornado F3, the air defence variant, there is no dedicated radar display. Navigation parameters and synthetic radar data are displayed on 2 large display screens in the rear cockpit instrument and panel. Moreover, although there are dedicated controls, all the essential combat functions can be controlled via a hand controller, which can easily be used while manoeuvring.

A mid-life update of the ground attack variant of the Tornado is currently under development and will enter service in 1998. The modernised aircraft will be designated Tornado GR4. Part of the update equips the aircraft with a forward-looking infra-red system which, together with night vision goggles, will enable the crew to see in the dark so they will be able to penetrate hostile territory covertly at low-level at night and in poor weather, without using the terrain following radar and will be able to find and attack targets without using the ground mapping radar. This will give a great improvement in their ability to survive hostile defences.

NAVIGATION TRAINING
The Royal Air Force has recently revised the organisation to train young men and women to become navigators on the variety of aircraft in current service. The navigator training structure is shown in Figure 1.

In essence, there is a common introductory phase of about 6 months, after which the trainee navigators are streamed into one of 3 specialisations, fast-jet, multi-engine or rotary wing for a rather longer period of advance training. Training takes place at 4 different locations – Cranwell, Topcliffe, Valley and Shawbury – but under the day-to-day control of the Officer Commanding the Navigator and Airmen Aircrew School at the Royal Air Force College, Cranwell. In more detail, training starts with basic groundschool, followed by 15 trips in the Bulldog at Cranwell and 21 trips in the faster Tucano at Topcliffe. This flying is mostly at low level, concentrating on basic visual navigation, track-keeping, procedures for attacking ground targets and for achieving the required time on target. Then, following a Leadership Training Expedition, there is a common core ground-school at Cranwell, leading into the advanced phase. This uses classroom instruction and simulator exercises to introduce the students to complex navigation equipment, radar systems and procedural navigation. The students are then streamed for fast-jets, multi-engine aircraft or helicopters.

NAVIGATOR TRAINING STRUCTURE

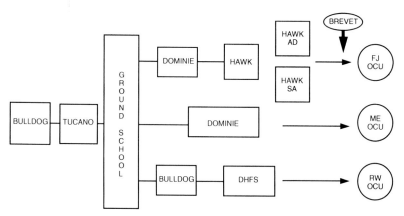

Figure 1

The fast-jet trainees remain at Cranwell initially for 15 flights and 6 simulator rides on the latest version of the Dominie, known as the Dominie Avionic Update. This has been designed to be very similar to the Tornado GR1 in radar performance and mechanisation of the navigation system, but with the ability to be adapted to represent other roles. There are 2 navigator stations with 14" colour displays. The radar picture is overlaid with the track, radar fix points, navaids, airfields and targets. This phase of training concentrates on radar handling and mission management. The students have to achieve accurate times-on-targets in spite of the instructor posing unplanned problems. At the end of this phase the scene shifts to Valley for 20 weeks of flying on the Hawk. This introduces the students to flying at 420kts in formation. Navigation is now secondary and this phase concentrates on airmanship, the mental air picture, lookout and formation and mission management. Air-to-air procedures and tactics are introduced and half-way through this phase the students are streamed into the "mud-moving" (ground attack) or air defence roles. At the end they are able to plan, brief, lead and debrief sorties by a pair of aircraft to achieve a combat task.

The multi-engine students remain at Cranwell on the Dominie for their advanced phase. This concentrates initially on the traditional navigation techniques of plotting and fixing, flight and fuel planning, airways flying and terminal procedures. Students are then streamed between either maritime (Nimrod) or the other multi-engine roles (air transport, air-to-air refuelling and AWACS). For the maritime students the Dominie display is configured similar to the Nimrod Tactical Screen and their training is geared to crew and mission management in flexible scenarios. Meanwhile the students destined for the air transport, air-to-air refuelling and AWACS roles concentrate on route and overseas navigation.

The rotary wing students initially remain at Cranwell on the Bulldog, where they are introduced to helicopter navigation techniques using large scale maps. They will then move to the new tri-Service Defence Helicopter Flying School at Shawbury. At the time of writing, the syllabus was not yet finalised, but it is likely to include a mix of single-engined helicopter flying for the essentials and an applied phase with pilot and air load master trainees in larger multi-engine helicopters and simulators.

Thus the training of today's navigators is less concerned with the business of how to determine where you are, and concentrates on crew co-operation, airmanship, mission management and the successful achievement of a military task. There is progressive streaming and specialisation so that successful students can make an easy transition to the next stage of training, which is operational conversion onto a particular front-line aircraft type. A wide variety of aircraft and simulators is used, and these are adapted to provide realistic representations of the type of flying the students will meet in the front line. At the end of about 15 months navigator training, with something like 120 hours flying under their belts and brevets proudly gleaming on their chests, the successful young men and women will move to the appropriate fast-jet, multi-engine or rotary wing operational conversion unit.

THE FUTURE
Technology
Looking to the future, and bearing in mind my earlier caveat that there is not a simple division between present and future, it seems to me that the greatest advances in the navigation/mission management are likely to come from exploiting three areas of technology: first, improvements in sensors; second, making more use of space and information derived from space; and third, enabling and underpinning everything, the ever-accelerating developments in computing and information technology.

Starting with sensors, we can expect the introduction of genuine multi-mode radars, which can simultaneously provide air-to-air and air-to-ground information. However, one current problem with radar is that, if an enemy detects your radar's transmissions, it alerts him to your presence. In the future, new modulation, power-management and signal processing techniques will be introduced to make it very difficult for an enemy to detect radar transmissions. Alternatively, attack aircraft may use microwave radar, which gives very high resolution and cannot be intercepted at long range. Another possibility is laser radar for obstacle avoidance at low level. Nevertheless, as discussed earlier, there will be increasing emphasis on the use of passive sensors, such as forward looking infra-red for situational awareness and target acquisition. Sensors will continue to become smaller, lighter and cheaper, with reduced power requirements, which will lead to much more widespread applications in weapons and unmanned air vehicles as well as manned aircraft.

I suggested at the beginning of this paper that the introduction of GPS was as significant an advance as Harrison's perfection of the chronometer. However, the exploitation of space has given much more to navigation/mission management than just GPS. It has provided reliable long range communication so essential to long-range operations and the style of expeditionary warfare, which seems likely to be the pattern for future UK operations. Anyone who has had to rely on the vagaries of HF communication will understand the significance of that advance. In addition, space technology has given us a much better understanding of the shape of the earth, which is of crucial importance to navigators. Satellite orbital data and measurements taken from satellites have provided very precise information about both the overall shape of the geoid and every bump and wrinkle on its surface. This data can be stored in digital form and fed into a

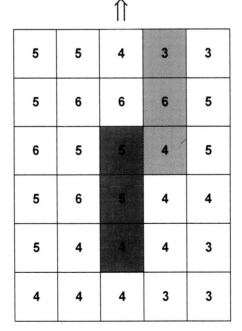

TERRAIN REFERENCE NAVIGATION
DATA COMPARISON

Figure 2

navigation system computer, so that the aircraft can carry, in effect, a very accurate 3-dimensional digital model of the part of the world it is flying over, which is much more useful than a 2-dimensional paper map. This precise data provides the key to enabling an aircraft to navigate precisely, with virtually no transmissions and independently of outside aids such as GPS, by direct reference to the shape of the earth over which it is flying. Terrain reference navigation is a very simple idea, which harnesses precise terrain data and the power of modern computing as illustrated in Figure 2.

Precise terrain elevation data are stored before flight in the aircraft's navigation system in the form of a close-grained matrix of spot heights, which gives a highly accurate 3-dimensional picture of the terrain over which the aircraft is planned to fly. In flight, the aircraft repeatedly measures height above terrain using a low-powered radar altimeter, which is difficult for hostile forces to detect. These measurements, when compared with the aircraft's altitude derived from a mix of barometric and inertial information, give a picture of the variation in the elevation of the terrain over which the aircraft is flying. The measurements are compared with the expected elevations at the aircraft's dead reckoning position (derived from inertial navigation information). The navigation computer correlates the measured data with the stored elevation to get the best fit and fixes the aircraft's position. In the example shown, the expected elevations are 4, 5, 5 whereas the measured values are 4, 6, 3; and the aircraft is further along track and to the right of the expected position. This fix is used to reset the navigation system position and after a suitable period the sequence is repeated. Given accurate enough data and adequate computing power this method can provide position to an accuracy comparable with GPS; it is completely self-contained and the only transmissions required can be made virtually undetectable. However, it can provide much more than position. As the system contains data on the precise shape of the surrounding terrain, it can provide ground collision avoidance; additional computing and display complexity would offer a passive terrain-following capability. Moreover, if the terrain database is overlaid with information on obstacles, such as masts and towers, it can also provide obstacle avoidance information. This form of terrain-following has two main advantages over terrain-following radar. First the aircraft does not broadcast its presence by transmitting on radar ahead of itself. Second, although terrain-following radar can tell you that there is high ground ahead, it cannot tell what is beyond it. On the other hand, the terrain database **does** know whether there is a plateau, a valley, or another hill over the next crest. In principle this would enable the aircraft's flight path to be tailored more closely to the terrain ahead and, thus would allow the aircraft to be flown closer to the ground than would be the case with terrain-following radar, improving its chances of surviving hostile defences. Indeed, the system could present the pilot or navigator with a synthetic picture of the terrain ahead, as seen from the cockpit, marked with the aircraft's planned (or optimum) flight path. This synthetic picture could be overlaid on the forward-looking infra-red scene in the pilot's head-up display and this combination would be a very powerful aid to flight close to the ground in the dark. The fixing and terrain collision avoidance modes of operation are starting to enter service, and I am confident that the more advanced capabilities will follow on in time.

Techniques like terrain reference navigation require the ability to store massive amounts of information and to carry out complex calculations in real time very accurately and with complete integrity. Thus they have only been made possible by the dramatic developments in computing and information technology, which are affecting every aspect of military business. This paper concentrates on three areas, which are relevant to tomorrow's navigators and pilots: the avionics in the cockpit; the wider dissemination of information around the battlespace; and mission planning.

Increasingly, the ability rapidly to process vast amounts of data allows information from a range of navigation and situation awareness sensors and their inputs to be integrated, combined and compared with stored data, and presented to aircrew in a user friendly fashion. Thus, in contrast to today's systems with separate IN, GPS and ILS equipment each with their own displays and controls, tomorrow's aircraft could have a single "black box" which integrates signals from laser inertial navigation gyros, GPS, GLONASS and microwave landing systems to produce extremely accurate position, velocity and steering information in three dimensions. The same box could also include a digital database of terrain and cultural data, including obstacles, airways and airfield terminal information. Another thrust of current research is to move away from "black boxes" which are dedicated to a single purpose, such as navigation, radar processing or weapon aiming to a system of general purpose processors, which exchange data by means of a very high speed data bus using optical signals. Such a system would be configured by software for a particular role and could be designed to reconfigure itself in flight, in the event of failure or battle damage, to undertake the highest priority tasks. Information would be displayed on general purpose displays, which automatically show what the pilot or navigator needs to see (and nothing else) at each phase of flight. Moreover, a great deal of work is going on to perfect helmet mounted displays, which will present navigation and sensor data to the aircrew on a screen in front of their eyes, wherever they are looking. Information on the helmet display will cue the navigator or pilot to visually acquire targets. Also the crew will be able to input targets to the system and slave sensors to targets merely by looking at them. Controls will be general purpose keyboards or, increasingly, hand controllers to enable hands on throttle and stick (HOTAS) operation. In addition the crew will be able to input data and control the system using voice commands.

The ability to process and transmit large quantities of information in near real time over long distances will enable sensors, platforms, weapons and command systems throughout the battlespace to be integrated together, in a seamless whole. Moreover the increased use of satellite communications will overcome line of sight problems, particularly for low flying aircraft. Thus, the individual aircraft crew might have the following information available over a variety of data links: updates to intelligence briefings; changes to tasking from the controlling authority; data from AWACS; information from electronic reconnaissance aircraft or unmanned air vehicles; and radar data from the new ground surveillance radar system, ASTOR, which is jointly sponsored by the British Army and the RAF, and due in service early next century. However, such a comprehensive data exchange system would not function without each of the participants knowing its position extremely accurately.

One of the first things I learned as a young navigator joining my first squadron was always to have a roll of maps in my car as evidence that I had just come from, or was just on the way to, the Flight Planning Section; we did spend a great deal of time there. I recall the long hours spent drawing up charts, calculating, checking and recalculating flight and fuel plans, pre-computing astro, working out initial point to target runs and so on. However, the chore of manual flight planning will soon be a thing of the past. Computer-based planning systems have been in service with Tornado for some time and the Harrier Advanced Mission Planning Aid, which entered service in 1996, is the first of a new generation of mission planning aids which will be used throughout the front line. In essence, an advanced mission planning aid consists of: a host computer; a store of relatively unchanging data such as digital terrain data, obstructions, aircraft aerodynamics, fuel consumption, weapon aiming and ballistics; an interface with command and information systems, which will input more ephemeral data such as intelligence, targets, mission details and weather; controls and displays to allow the navigator or pilot to interact with the system; an output medium; and software to undertake the mission planning task. Given a very few essential inputs, such as the target and weapon load, the mission planning aid automatically plans the entire mission, including the target attack run and weapon release parameters, choosing the optimum flight profile; for example, it can pick a route to fly which offers minimum risk from enemy defences. It displays the mission pictorially to the navigator or pilot during the planning process to enable him to make choices or override the system decision. The mission planning aid outputs all the details of the mission onto a data transfer cartridge, which is taken out to the aircraft and plugged in to automatically transfer the data into the aircraft system. It can also print out a coloured route map annotated with details of the mission, which can be carried as a back-up to the navigation computer. Some systems can also show a three-dimensional view of the route which enables the crew to visualise the most critical parts of the mission, such as the run-in to the target, before they take off. The main advantages of these systems are that they significantly reduce planning time and virtually eliminate human error in both calculations and data entry. They can provide a complete planning, briefing and debriefing system. With two-way exchange of information they could be used by a superior headquarters for programming and tasking all the elements of an operation.

FUTURE SYSTEMS

Turning from technology to actual systems, the descriptions in the following paragraphs of three aircraft which will enter service – the

C-130J, the Nimrod 2000 and Eurofighter – illustrate what is just around the corner.

The C-130J, which will enter service in 1997 is fairly typical of the trend in multi-engine aircraft navigation. It does not have a navigator, nor a flight engineer for that matter. The cockpit contains four large multi-function displays, which the pilots will use to fly and navigate the aircraft. The navigation systems consist of: twin inertial navigation systems with imbedded Global Positioning System; a Doppler navigator; a weather and mapping radar; radar altimeter; TACAN, VOR and ADF. There is also provision for a precision airfield approach system to be fitted once it is clear which system the civil aviation authorities intend to adopt. All of these systems are controlled through multi-purpose keyboards and the information is displayed on the four multi-function displays, which also provide attitude information and 'housekeeping' data on engines, fuel, hydraulics, electrics and so on. The aircraft has Head-Up Displays for low level flight; it is probably the first transport aircraft to be equipped with these. Forward-looking infra-red may be fitted later. Although the aircraft will normally be operated by just 2 pilots, there is a third seat on the flight deck, with its own keyboard access to the navigation and flight control system. This provides the option of carrying a third member of flight deck crew to share the load on the most demanding missions.

In Nimrod 2000 (the replacement Maritime Patrol Aircraft) the navigator, the tactical co-ordinator, the radar operator, and the sonar operators will all have identical multi-purpose display screens and computer keyboards. Each crew station will be virtually identical and the operator will 'log on' to tell the system that he is the navigator, the radar operator or the sonar operator. Most of the navigation functions will be automated so the navigator will also take on the duties of the communicator.

The Eurofighter is central to plans for the Royal Air Force front line. Its navigation system, like much else about the aircraft, will represent the definitive standard in the early years of the next century. Figure 3 shows the 'Active Cockpit' rig, which is being used in the Eurofighter development programme. As can be seen, the Eurofighter cockpit is dominated by three large multi-function display screens. Each display screen can show a wide range of data; for example attitude; moving map, fuel; radar data; the navigation plot; a situation

display based on JTIDS data-link information; or details of the
weapon load. Each type of information can be displayed on any of the
screens, and routine information, such as fuel or engine performance,
is only displayed when it is needed or asked for. There are 'soft' keys
around the edges of each display screen; their purpose and captions
change according to the information displayed. However, the pilot
can control all essential functions through switches and controls on
the throttle and stick. There is also a wide-angle Head-Up Display
and the pilot will be equipped with a Display Helmet, which will
show information wherever he is looking. The heart of the navigation
system in Eurofighter is a Laser Inertial Navigation System with an
integrated GPS. Data from these and other sensors, such as data-link,
radar, forward-looking infra-red and terrain reference ground
collision avoidance, are compared, filtered and cross-monitored
before being presented to the pilot. High levels of accuracy will be
achieved without the need for manual fixing, allowing the pilot to

Figure 3: The British Aerospace 'Active Cockpit'
(photograph courtesy of British Aerospace, Military Aircraft Division)

devote his attention to the key mission tasks in the knowledge that the navigation system will be accurate.

WEAPONS

Aircraft need good weapons to be effective. In the air-to-ground role, increasing use is being made of long-range autonomous weapons, which can fly hundreds of kilometres to a target and hit it with great accuracy. The Royal Air Force has recently decided to buy the British Aerospace/Matra Storm Shadow to equip its Tornados and Eurofighters. These long-range autonomous weapons need to navigate their way across the earth, avoiding obstacles and hostile defences, and then find their targets, in very much the same way as a manned aircraft is navigated. Therefore they make use of similar navigation aids, such as the Global Positioning System and Terrain Reference Systems, together with attitude height and air data sensors and an autopilot, and they may use sensors such as radar and forward-looking infra-red to find their targets and identify precise aiming points. Their missions need to be planned as thoroughly as an aircraft mission, using similar computer-based mission planning aids.

FUTURE TRENDS – WHITHER THE NAVIGATOR?

Where is all this leading? Let me suggest three ways in which we could exploit the increasing power of information technology even more. The first is mission rehearsal on the ground. Current aircraft crew simulators are quite realistic, but they are used mainly for prac-tising procedures and drills, which are either too dangerous or too expensive to practice in the air, for example emergency procedures. However they have the potential to do much more. If future simulators used the real-world terrain data and intelligence, as used in mission planning systems, it would be possible for crews to rehearse actual missions before they flew them. Moreover, linking simulators together, either through a local area network on an airbase, or a wide area network between air bases, would allow all the crews in a formation to rehearse the mission together. It is hoped that the Eurofighter synthetic training system will have this capability.

The second area is cockpit developments. The ultimate develop-ment of all the work that is being done on displays might be to produce a system which is able to give the crew such a good synthetic picture of the outside world that they would not need to look outside.

A fast-jet cockpit without windows would have three main advantages: it would protect the crew from weapons such as lasers without the need to sit up to see out, the crew's seats could be designed so that they were virtually lying on their backs, which would increase their tolerance to G forces; and it would allow more efficient aerodynamic designs of aircraft. There is research work going on in several countries into the so-called virtual cockpit.

If the outside world could be faithfully presented to someone sitting in an enclosed cockpit, it could also be transmitted on a data link to someone sitting in comfort back at base allowing him or her to control the aircraft remotely. Therefore it seems to me that unmanned air vehicles are another area where significant advances may be expected. Unmanned air vehicles, both autonomous and remotely piloted, have been in service for some time, mainly for reconnaissance. However, some experts now suggest that modern technology will soon be good enough to replace the crew completely, allowing unmanned bomber or fighter aircraft. This would offer the following advantages: first it would reduce or eliminate aircrew casualties; second, aircraft without the need to carry human beings and all their life support systems would be smaller and cheaper; and aircraft performance would not be constrained by human tolerance; for example G-limits. It also raises the question: "Whither the Navigator?" Unmanned bomber and fighter aircraft would clearly not require a navigator, but are they a realistic prospect in the foreseeable future? Readers are reminded that what follows are my personal views. I have no doubt that there will be an increasing use of unmanned air vehicles for reconnaissance and possibly other tasks such as air to ground weapons delivery. However, I am doubtful of the prospect of unmanned bomber or fighter aircraft completely replacing manned aircraft in the Royal Air Force front line in my lifetime. For a start, there would be the considerable technical challenge of perfecting such a fool-proof system, with completely reliable data links which cannot be spoofed or jammed. My doubt is also based on much more fundamental arguments. Conflict and combat are essentially human activities to do with breaking the will of your opponent by the use of surprise and ingenuity as well as the use of force; and this has everything to do with being on the spot to exploit opportunities and adapt plans to match changing circumstances, rather than being hundreds of miles away, sat in front of a television screen. Manned aircraft provide flexibility both during and between missions because of the powers of reasoning and adaptability of their crews. The flexibility of the human mind exploiting the third dimension is a priceless asset, which has proved crucial to victory in every theatre of war since man first took to the air. I do not believe that it can be replaced by machine. Although we will continue to exploit technology to the full to **help** the human mind. Planning has already started for a Tornado Replacement, provisionally called the Future Offensive Aircraft. If we assume that there will be another generation of combat aircraft after Eurofighter, will they be single-seat or two-seat aircraft? There are clear economies in single seat operation, but, notwithstanding the power of modern computers to help a pilot, a long range attack mission deep into enemy territory – the most taxing mission for a future offensive aircraft – is a highly complex undertaking. Moreover, all our experience seems to suggest that the more help we give the man in the cockpit in the way of computer assistance, the more we expect him to do. So a two-man crew would be less likely to be working to capacity and thus would be more effective and, importantly, more flexible on a long range mission. Furthermore, long-range flight in hostile territory in a single-seat aircraft is very lonely; anecdotal evidence from operations in the Gulf War confirms the value in morale terms of two-man crews.

Meanwhile, in large aircraft, such as maritime patrol and AWACS, there is a clear and continuing role for navigators. Their duties are likely to become increasingly broad and I believe that we may see the navigation and air electronics specialisations merging together. Thus, while I cannot be certain of what the future holds for the navigator, I believe that reports of his imminent demise are much exaggerated.

12. Afternoon Discussion Period

Chairman's Introduction

Before we continue with the final Discussion period, we have here today Walter Blanchard, who is the President of the Royal Institute of Navigation, and I would just like him to say a few words to us.

WALTER BLANCHARD:

Good afternoon, Ladies and Gentlemen. I think that this is what they call the 'commercial slot'. Many of you here, I know, are already members of the Royal Institute of Navigation; but perhaps one or two of you are not, and are not sure what it is for and what it does. The RIN was formed in 1947 because of a perceived need to advance the science of navigation. We heard a little about what state that had fallen into in the pre-1939 period this morning. We look at both marine and air navigation and now, of course, land navigation as well; and we try to advance the state of the art through educating people, by promoting knowledge of the state of navigation itself and by encouraging the use of new systems.

Bill Tyack was wondering whether the navigator would be needed in the future and gave us a very good answer to that, which I would support. As a humble squadron navigator myself, many years ago, I am glad to have his assurance that navigators may be around for some time yet. I have a 17-year-old daughter who has just got an RAF Flying Scholarship and is thinking of following in her father's footsteps at some point. Anyway there are still many things to do. SATNAV is a great thing and a tremendous technical advance, but the point that is often missed is that, in the excitement of this new technology we tend to forget that somebody has to own, operate and control those systems; and the methods of doing that are not always obvious. We have found in the RIN over the last few years that there is a great deal of education to do in that sphere. The ownership and control of a lot of the civil systems has been predicated on the basis that you can control it from within your own country; but with SATNAV you cannot do that. So, in addition to what Bill said, I think that not only the navigator but the Institute is going to be required for a bit longer yet.

We have been delighted to be associated with the Historical Society today. I have learnt a lot: I always enjoy these Society meetings, and I hope that maybe one or two of you who feel that the RIN is worth supporting will come and join us. Thank you very much

CHAIRMAN:

Happily we have also got with us today the Master-Elect of the Guild of Air Pilots and Air Navigators, Ron Bridge. Perhaps, Ron, you would also like to say a few words to us.

RON BRIDGE

Thank you very much. GAPAN, just like the Royal Institute of Navigation, is very glad to be associated with the RAF Historical Society in this presentation on Navigation. For those of you who do not know what the Guild is all about, it is a Livery Company of the City of London. We got our Charter in 1956 and were the 81st, so that it took 800 years to get to 81: and now after only a further 40 years there are 101, which goes to show how fast things are moving.

Anyway, a lot of people have misconceptions about us. The biggest problem I find is that civil pilots and the few civil navigators that are left think that GAPAN is entirely an RAF operation; and all the Service people that I talk to think that it is a civil operation. Hopefully we can all get together. Thank you very much indeed.

CHAIRMAN

We have nearly half an hour to continue with our discussion and question period. We have the afternoon speakers here, but we still retain the morning speakers; so let the discussion range over the whole gamut of what we have been talking about.

ANON: The Terrain-Referenced Navigation Systems: how is the basic data collected?

Air Cdre BILL TYACK: Essentially from observing satellite orbits and from reconnaissance data. Nowadays there are civil satellites, which are providing information that is probably accurate enough for a basic system.

Air Cdre NORMAN BONNOR: Felton and the U.S. equivalent developed a digital data-base matrix for radar simulation in training Tornado and F-111 crews. They rapidly realised that it could be used for many other things, such as a cruise missile fixing system, siting of SAM systems and radio-communication link planning; and so it has grown. Now virtually the whole world is mapped for terrain-elevation data, with feature data on as well; so that you can have a genuine digital map. The prime data base is held in Washington.

PETER HEARNE (RIN): I wanted to agree with two points in Air Commodore Tyack's talk. First, as a former Systems Supplier, I certainly can never see a system replacing a human being in front-line combat aircraft: the flexibility of the human being is absolutely essential. We cannot make systems clever enough to adapt themselves immediately to the sort of situations that might occur. The second was on the question of will there be a future navigator? I think that the amount of computing power and the additional information that we can pump through the data-links mean that you need two people in the aeroplane just to absorb it all. We are already seeing that in single-seat aircraft the pilot will be overloaded.

Gp Capt HANS NEUBROCH: The V-Force and the U.S. Navigation and Bombing Competition; in which we did rather well I believe. Would the panel comment on that? Also, we heard about pre-War inter-theatre deployments. What about post-War? I recall that 11 Squadron deployed eight single-seat aircraft non-stop from Leuchars to Changi in 1969 or '70. The limitations were oil capacity and physiological ones, such as sleep and being so long in a semi-recumbent position. The flight plan was done in co-ordination with the Tanker Force by a rather clever young Lightning pilot on his first staff tour, by the name of Squadron Leader Mike Graydon.

BONNOR: I had a bad experience to do with the Bombing Competition: my crew and others at Wittering were due to go in 1965. We had trained with special sorties to check how the aircraft performed on the dreadful, and more volatile, fuel used over there. One of our slipper tanks decided to jettison its fuel as we took off, and we had about 100 feet of flame behind us. But just before we were due to go the Victor developed wing cracks. The Vulcans did extremely well over the years, despite not being in the role that they would have operated in the UK environment, I can't really tell you why we were good at it, except that small is always beautiful, I suppose, compared to Strategic Air Command.

AVM MICHAEL ROBINSON: I don't think that we actually won in America, because it was highly political. We certainly won over here, because we designed 'the course for the horse'. I will not forget the story of one of our umpires in a B-52. They set off exactly on track, well out into the North Sea, and were coming back into Scotland where they had to do a very quick turn, not being accurate either in position or time; and the whole trip got worse and worse. Why? The navigator in a B-52 had his own personal computer, and had totally forgotten the art of mental calculation. His computer batteries had run out, and he had no spares. So beware about being totally reliant on the computer!

AVM NIGEL BALDWIN: I was going to call on my SASO to speak; and he has just done so. My view changed during my time with the Vulcan squadrons. If I and my crew were part of the 10% of the elite who were involved, we thought it was a jolly good thing; but if not we did not think that it was a good thing at all. Now, on balance I think that the commanders were right because it sharpened us all up.

BONNOR: Techniques were often developed specially for bombing competitions and this did sharpen things up, including the servicing. Not just the American, but our own Bomber Command Competition back here in the UK. The effort that went in was always well used later; and the other crews gained from it.

Gp Capt COLIN PARRY (RIN): Three things. The first is that I am not going to be rude about SAC. The second is that when I was on No. 11 Spec N course we were graced by Air Marshal Kyle, subsequently C-in-C Bomber Command, who was then ACAS OR. He came on after the person who was talking about the NVS System in the V Force; and he pointed out, in his rather blunt Australian way, that the thing that he had seen work best with a bullet in it was a human being. The third thing is that when the TSR2 was coming in, it was such an advance that there was an awful lot of work done on the psycho-medical evaluation of crew. Becoming serious now, information overload has been mentioned. Are we doing anything in these more modern aircraft to assess the psychological and medical situations which we are putting the crew into, particularly in the single-seat aircraft?

TYACK: The simple answer is 'Yes': there is a lot of work going on both on the physiological side of flying an aircraft like the Eurofighter and on the human factor. It is an area where I think we thought that we were doing rather better than the other Services. We have always had aircrew involved in cockpit design and so on, but there is still much to learn and we have to keep working at it. The Eurofighter is a very good example of a system designed to show you only the information you need at a particular phase of flight; so that you could do an entire flight and never see an engine RPM or temperature or fuel gauge, because if they work correctly you don't need to see them and there are, therefore, no distractions. A nice female voice will tell you when you get to Bingo fuel, and you will turn home. But the real challenge is that with all the aids we expect people to do more and more, and we have to keep working to avoid people getting overload.

PARRY: If I can just come back on that. There was a recent case of a civil aircraft that had to land because a second pilot said that he did not want to fly any more. Have we reached that stage, and have we some idea how we might avoid it?

ANON: 'Tubby' Vielle gave him the right answer, I think. (Note: Group Captain E. E. 'Tubby' Vielle is a 1939 Spec. N who, following the incident referred to, was interviewed by the Daily Telegraph on the subject).

BONNOR: Every time that we have built an aircraft, dammit if we haven't changed its role several times before it went out of service; and the only way that we have actually achieved that, apart from tinkering with equipment, is the adaptability of the people flying it: that has been vital. I think the V Force was a prime example: all the roles and techniques used over its years of service could only be achieved with men in the cockpit. There was no other way of doing it.

TYACK: I must say emphatically that we have not got to the position in the RAF where there are people who don't want to go flying. More seriously, when I was DOR (Air) I had a lot of young men working for me who had flown in the Gulf and, subsequently, over Bosnia and so on; and the Tornado got a bad press in the Gulf. I asked every one of them "What was the Tornado like to go to war in?" To a man they replied that they would go to war in it again tomorrow.

STUART MILLSTEAD: I am not a navigator or in the RAF, but am playing 'Devil's Advocate' in the man versus machine argument. In civil aviation some 300 people don't want to fly around in a machine with no man controlling it. In military flying, assuming that a suitable data-link exists, there must be an argument for removing the stress by placing the operator several hundred or even just fifty miles away from his machinery. If there is a mistake and it gets blown to bits, then he is not going to go with it. It seems to me, as a layman, that everyone here has a vested interest – past or present – in being in an aircraft and, perhaps that is blocking the view a bit. I don't actually believe that; so before I get lynched on the way out . . .

TYACK: I don't want to hog the answers, but there are lots of arguments for keeping people there. Combat is basically between people, and in a tense situation the adrenaline starts running and many people perform much better than sitting somewhere in an armchair in a bunker miles away from the action. The best synthetic system in the world will not re-create the actual atmosphere. Another aspect is the whole question of Rules of Engagement in a foreseeable future conflict: not a fight for survival, – the Bosnia or Gulf type of involvement. There is great concern on the part of the politicians on minimising casualties, particularly among non-combatants: you can design a perfectly good weapons system to go and blow a bridge apart, but it cannot tell you whether there are refugees streaming across it. Whereas the crew of an aircraft going in for their final attack would see that.

MILLSTEAD: They would have the same information as they would have in a remote-control situation.

TYACK: Well, what happens if the data-link breaks? The politician is going to ask "OK Air Marshal, before we launch this sortie what are the odds of innocent civilians getting involved?" Theoretically it can be foolproof, but if there is a chance of it not working a politician will shy away from it. Another aspect is the cost-benefit analysis: with the manned aircraft you have the greater flexibility.

MILLSTEAD: I was making a distinction between automatic and remote-controlled aircraft.

AM SIR JOHN CURTISS: I think that like everything else in life there is a place for more than one kind of weapon, and there are certain targets which require the Tomahawk approach and others which require the manned approach. I was a bit surprised visiting Lyneham last week to be told that the J will not carry a navigator, or even a third person, they think. Whereas, if you speak to the crews, particularly those who are engaged in low-level special forces work, they will all tell you adamantly that a third man in that aeroplane – engineer, navigator, call him what you like, is essential: and I just worry that with the current drive for economy this is going to end up as an aeroplane which is not as fully flexible and capable, simply because they have gone back on having two crew.

After two tours on night fighters there is not the slightest doubt in my mind that you need a two-seat aeroplane for that job; and I know all the arguments about flexibility and cost reduction. You are asking the Eurofighter to do just about everything; and it only needs a bit of degradation in one of the systems, and the poor pilot is going to have a real problem on his hands. I was delighted to hear that my successors down the line, like Bill Tyack here, still believe in the two-man concept.

ANON: Does the RAF have a fixation about low-level? In the Gulf the Americans seemed to be going for high and medium level.

TYACK: I think that the answer is that if you design a system to operate at low-level, provided you ensure that it can also operate at medium and higher levels, then you can fly there. The lesson from the Gulf War is that you need to be able to do both. If there is a hill to hide behind then that is a better place to be; but there is a place for everything, and I don't see low-level as an absolute panacea, but it is a capability that we have got to keep in our armoury.

I absolutely agree on the two-man, three-man thing in the J. One thing that came through in the operational requirement was a seat and controls so that the capability is there to put a third person on the flight-deck if and when needed. It is a case of persuading the authorities to pay for those extra people on the squadrons. The longer and more demanding missions will certainly have three people on the flight-deck.

CURTISS: I think that we have learnt subsequently that there has been some misunderstanding about the Tornado and the Gulf War. If you talk to the American Commanders they will tell you that the only squadrons that could actually do what was required, that is, taking out Iraqi airfields the size of Heathrow, were the Tornados with their particular weapons system going in low. Yes, they suffered some unfortunate casualties, but they were pretty small compared to back in the 40s. The flexibility of air power is its single biggest advantage, and the more flexibility you can build into a system the better: which is why some of us old fogeys still believe in people as well as computers.

COLIN BELL: On that subject I can give three very quick examples. Twice on my first squadron within six months had we had only one person, or none at all, the vehicle would have crashed, because we were directed by the ground to do things which were clearly stupid: the pilots were respectively a Pole and a Czech. But a more important example was during Suez. First, we had all the fancy equipment in our Canberras but it was intended for European operations. Rapidly someone put in some radio compasses but, unfortunately they switched off the radios so that they were not going to be much use. We were informed of a change of target, since American civilians were being evacuated from Cairo West: so we broadcast 'Valiant Watney Marker' do not bomb Cairo West, bomb Almaza'; and Almaza called us back and said "Your QDM is 189". When we actually got there I was in the number two aircraft: the first dropped his flares, and I then noticed that we were not over the right target but were actually over Cairo International and, lo and behold, all the IL 28s were immediately beneath us. So we bombed Cairo International; and it was the most successful raid of the War. Now I don't think that decision could have been made by a totally automatic system. It was the human beings, there were four of us in the team, who sorted it.

DR BILL HOWELL (RIN): I was at a meeting of anaesthetists a while ago, which was a symposium on nausea with anaesthesia. There was a chap there from the RAF who told us that he was investigating the problem of nausea; because they had found that there was hardly any nausea with high-level bombing, but with low-level bombing there was a significant increase in nausea which incapacitated the flyers.

13. The Chairman's Concluding Remarks

It only leaves me now to draw these proceedings to a close. It is not the Chairman's job in a symposium of this nature to draw conclusions. What we have actually heard here is the entire History of Air Navigation since its inception to what we see now as one of systems; although it was gratifying to hear that so many people believe that the man in the system is still vital, at least in military aviation. So all I really want to do is to say how very grateful I am to Philip Saxon, who has been instrumental in putting the symposium together, and also to each and every one of our speakers today who have given us such an extraordinarily interesting insight into a particular aspect of the nearly 100 years of aerial navigation. I also want to thank all of you people who have brought your own expertise to this subject and have provided what has been, at least for me, a fascinating day. Thank you all for coming. Thank you again to my speakers.

Biographical Notes

AIR MARSHAL SIR JOHN CURTISS KCB KBE FRAeS

Sir John Curtiss joined the Oxford University Air Squadron in 1942 and, having trained as a navigator, served in Bomber Command on 578 and 158 Squadrons (Halifaxes) in 1944/45. He then flew with a series of squadrons in Transport Command, which included the Berlin Airlift. After a period on Fighter Control duties he served with 29 Squadron (Meteor night fighters) and 5 Squadron (Javelins). He became Wing Commander Flying at Wittering, a V-Force station; then Station Commander. He commanded Bruggen, became Group Captain Operations at Strike Command, was SASO at 11 Group and served as Commandant at the Staff College. He next became AOC of 18 (Maritime) Group, and was Air Commander of the Falklands Task Force. He retired from the RAF in 1983, having served in all the operational Commands.

From 1984 to 1989 he was Director and Chief Executive of the Society for British Aerospace Companies; and has since served a number of prominent charities, as well as holding office in the Pathfinder, Aircrew and Bomber Command Associations.

D M PAGE FRIN

Master Mariner; served in the Merchant Navy 1945-57. Received initial flying training as a Royal Naval Reserve Officer, and in 1957 came ashore to join Civil Aviation. In 1959 became Chief Navigator for one of the parent companies of British Caledonian Airways and for over thirty years held Senior Aircrew Management posts, concerned with the efficient navigation and operation of a fleet of aircraft which evolved from the Avro York and Tudor to the second and third generation of jets. Authorised CAA Navigator Flight Test Examiner and Aircraft Flight Test Observer.

A Fellow and former Vice-President of the Royal Institute of Navigation, has served as Chairman of a number of International

Aviation Technical Committees; and has represented the airlines at ICAO on navigational matters, including the recent Future Air Navigation Systems Committee.

Currently Chairman of the RIN Technical Committee, David Page has always had an interest in the history of navigation and in the means whereby the mariners passed on their skills to the airmen; and now notes, with a certain amusement, that regarding a systems approach to navigation and bridge layout the mariners are now learning from the airmen.

FLIGHT LIEUTENANT ALEC AYLIFFE
MBE MA MRIN

After reading Modern History at Oxford, Alec joined the RAF in 1975 to be a navigator on historic aircraft. He has completed flying tours on Shackleton AEW, Nimrod MR1, Nimrod MR2 and, as a navigation instructor, on Dominie TMk1 aircraft. He is a graduate of the Staff Navigation Course the General Duties Aerosystems Course. From 1990 to 1993, he was a trials officer with the Central Tactics and Trials Organisation (CTTO) Long Range Maritime Patrol Cell, at Northwood; undertaking a number of radar, electro-optic and magnetic anomaly detection trials on Nimrod MR2 aircraft.

He has just completed a tour, at the Military Survey Defence Agency, as a staff officer responsible for arranging the supply of digital geographic information to the RAF. He was also the Project Manager for the Digital Geographic Processing and Preparation System (DIGPAPS); relating to aircraft cockpit displays and mission support systems. He is now serving at the Defence Trials and Evaluation Organisation (DTEO) at Boscombe Down, as a Missions System Trials Officer and manager of the Large Aircraft Laboratory (currently an historic Comet 4).

WING COMMANDER C G JEFFORD MBE
BA

'Jeff' joined the RAF in 1959 as a pilot, but it soon became apparent that there were flaws in the selection system and he (was) remustered as a navigator the following year. His flying experience, during which he accumulated some 3,500 flying hours, included a tour on Canberras with No. 45 Squadron at Tengah, two lengthy stints on Vulcans with Nos 83 and 50 Squadrons and an instructional tour with No. 6 FTS. Administrative and air staff appointments involved sundry jobs at Manby, Gatow, HQ Support Command and a total of eight years at HQ Strike Command. He took early retirement in 1991 to go back to school, graduating from London University with First Class Honours in History three years later. He has two books to his credit: – 'RAF Squadrons' (1988), which is regarded as a valuable work of reference, and 'The Flying Camels' (1995), a History of 45 Squadron, both of which books were meticulously researched. Jeff is the son of an RAF officer and married the daughter of another: he, his father and his father-in-law notched up 107 years of service between them.

SQUADRON LEADER PHILIP SAXON MA
MRIN

Philip Saxon joined the RAF as a u/t observer in 1941 (after a spell as a student engineer at the Bristol Aeroplane Company occasioned by his brother's death in Bomber Command in early 1940). He was commissioned from Air Navigation School in South Africa and, after AFU and OTU in the UK, was (1943) posted to 216 (Transport) Group in the Middle East. He served on No. 1 ADU (later 5 FU) until January 1945: flying the Takoradi route, round the Med to Italy, Gib, Malta, Greece and Turkey and the route to India; in many types of aircraft – and with many nationalities of pilot, and frequently leading convoys. He became Unit Navigation Officer; and then attended a Staff Navigation Course at Shawbury ("distinguished pass') from Feb to May 1945. Returning to 216 Group, he became a Wing Navigation Officer based successively at Khartoum, Aden and Habbaniya. His final post was Senior Operations Officer at Almaza Airport. After demob in 1946 he went up to Cambridge to read Mathematics and History, and run for the University. His career in industry from 1949 to 1986 saw him working for a number of well-known companies, latterly as a non-executive director. In retirement he has continued his life-long interest in athletics as an official, but ran a number of marathons in his early sixties (p.b. 3 hours 24 mins): in his seventies he has been reduced to marathon charity swims. During this period he has also pursued his interest in history and, in particular, the history of the RAF. He is currently researching 'A History of Specialist Navigation Training in the RAF'.

GROUP CAPTAIN D W BROUGHTON MBE
BA FRIN
David Broughton joined the RAF in 1960 and, after navigator training, served in the Medium Range Transport force on Argosies at Benson and Khormaksar. Subsequent Staff Navigation training led to his retention at CAW Manby as Avionics Specialist, following which he became a student of the 1970 GD ASC. Next a tour at A&AEE; then back on the ASC Staff – now at Cranwell – first as Course Commander and then as Senior Avionics Specialist. On completion of the Canberra OCU in 1978 he moved to RAE Bedford as Senior Operations Officer; and latterly OC Radar Research Squadron (with 21 aircraft and just 7 crews!). The NDC course saw him into MOD in 1982 as the data-link specialist on the C31S Central Staff, but in 1984 he escaped back to flying as OC Nimrod AEW Joint Trials Unit – an A&AEE team detached to Waddington. Then, following the AWC, he was posted back to MOD as Ops AEW. His final posting was back to the C31S Central Staffs as AD for Policy; he retired after the Gulf War in 1991.

David had been an active Member of the Royal Institute of Navigation from the early 1970s and, on leaving the RAF, became its Director. He is also a Special Lecturer on Navigation Technology at Nottingham University. He has been closely associated with Aries flights, having 25 under his belt – of which all but two have reached the North Geographic Pole.

AIR VICE-MARSHAL JACK FURNER CBE
DFC AFC FIMgt FIPD

Jack Furner joined the RAF in 1941 and entered Bomber Command in late 1942: his first tour was on Stirlings and his second on Fortresses. In early 1945 he transferred to Transport Command in the Far East, supporting the Burma front line in Dakotas. After VJ he distributed supplies, collected POWs and delivered VIPs around the South East Asia area. Returning home in 1947, he instructed at a Navigation School; then attended No. 9 Spec N at CNCS Shawbury from July 1950 to April 1951. He was then posted to Boscombe Down where he carried out trials of new equipment and, subsequently, at Wright Air Development Centre, Dayton, Ohio. Back home in 1956 he was made OC Operations Wing at RAF Waddington, the first Vulcan station: then to HQ Bomber Command for War Planning, and on to SHAPE in the Nuclear Activities Branch. In 1965 he was made a Deputy Director of Manning in the Air Ministry and then given command of RAF Scampton, housing three Vulcan/Blue Steel Squadrons. In 1969 he became the last commander of the Central Reconnaissance Establishment, and in 1970 was appointed as Secretary to the Military Committee in NATO HQ Brussels. He completed his service as Assistant Air Secretary, overseeing the careers of all officers up to the rank of Group Captain. In 1973 he became Chairman of the Spec N Association, shortly after to become the Aries Association. He retired in 1976. During his 35 years in the Service, he flew in 42 different aircraft types with 243 different pilots; the aircraft included single-, twin-, 4-, 6-, 8-, and 10-engined types.

AIR COMMODORE NORMAN BONNOR
FRIN FRAeS

Norman Bonnor joined the RAF as a Cranwell cadet in 1957. He did two operational tours as a navigator on Victor aircraft. After Staff Navigation and Spec N. courses, he was a System Trials Section Leader at AETE in Canada, then Project Officer Phantom Avionics at MOD(PE). This was followed in 1972 by Staff College at Bracknell and spells as an

Instructor at the College of Air Warfare at Manby and on the Tornado Specification Team at RAE Farnborough. From 1976-80 he was Project manager Nimrod MR Mk2 refit at MOD(PE), after which he attended the Air Warfare Course at Cranwell. He was then successively Chief Experimental Navigation Officer at Boscombe Down; Deputy Director Navigation Services at MOD; Officer Commanding RAF Waddington and Deputy Director Operational Requirements (Air) 6 at MOD. From 1988 to 1990, when he left the RAF, he served as Chief of Staff and Deputy Commander, NATO Airborne Early Warning Force. On retirement he was Director of Business Development – Europe for GEC-Marconi Electronic Systems Corporation of New Jersey. Currently he manages and lectures on a post-graduate course in navigation technology at the University of Nottingham.

AIR COMMODORE E W TYACK CBE FRAeS RAF
Bill Tyack is the Senior Military Officer in the Defence Evaluation and Research Agency. He was born in 1944 and joined the RAF in 1962. After completing navigator training he served in Coastal Command flying Shackletons on Nos 210 and 42 Squadrons. Between 1971 and 1976 he served at Boscombe Down managing and taking part in flight trials on weapons systems and avionics for a range of aircraft. Staff tours at the Ministry of Defence followed, in the Operational Requirements, Personnel Management and Forward Policy (RAF) branches. He commanded No. 51 Squadron (Nimrod R) from 1983 to 1985. After a short tour in the Defence Concepts Staff, he commanded RAF Wyton from 1987 to 1989, flying Canberra and Nimrod aircraft. He then served as an Assistant Director in the Defence Commitments (NATO) staff before attending the Royal College of Defence Studies in 1992; followed by three years as the Director of Operational Requirements (Air Systems) in the MOD. He then undertook a six-month study to write British Defence Doctrine, before taking up his present appointment in September 1996. He is a graduate of the Staff Navigation, General Duties Aerosystems, Royal Naval Staff and Air Warfare Courses; and has some 5,000 flying hours. Bill is the current President of the Aries Association.

'Dickie' Richardson's Contribution to RAF Navigation

Preface by Philip Saxon

Whilst on demobilisation leave in the summer of 1946 I found myself in London and, not having yet made the decision as to whether or not I might remain in the RAF, I visited the Air Ministry to seek the advice of the then Director of Navigation, Air Commodore 'Gil' Saye. In the event he was not available and I saw his Deputy, Group Captain 'Dickie' Richardson; whom I had last met at Shawbury some eighteen months previously. I remember the conversation vividly. Dickie said "What will you do if you don't stay in the Air Force?" "Go up to Cambridge University", I said. "I'd do that", said Dickie. Thus was my future determined.

When, nearly fifty years later, I was carrying out research on the History of Navigation in the RAF, Dickie was one of those Spec. Ns whom I approached for support and advice. This was something that he was never loath to provide; though his views were often trenchant. Later, in August, 1995, he wrote me a letter which included the following: "I am worried that the subject is really not suitable for a one-day seminar" . . . "I fear one day's discussion cannot possibly do justice to this subject, which deals with a metamorphosis equivalent to the span between the Ice Age and the Space Age".

Nevertheless, I am sure that he would have enjoyed the day; though he would doubtless have had some forthright observations to make during the Discussion period. Over the years Dickie had made a major contribution to navigation in the RAF and it seems appropriate that in this History he should have the last word.

No history of navigation in the RAF would be complete without the inclusion of 'Dickie' Richardson – Group Captain F C Richardson – who was one of the moving spirits behind this Seminar but is now (we feel sure) teaching the Angels to find their way around the celestial regions; for, sadly, he died in October 1995. But he has left a testament – an autobiography which is due to be published in 1997 – which puts on record his many significant contributions to RAF navigation, most notably his authorship of that classic book Air Navigation, published as AP1234.

Dickie (as he was always known) joined the RAF in 1933 on a Short Service commission and was immediately posted to Egypt – as was the custom in those days – for flying training. He was taught to fly on Avro 504Ns at No. 4 Flying Training School, Abu Sueir, near Ismailia. After five months and 75 hours' flying he graduated to the Armstrong Whitworth Atlas.

He summed-up his training as "of a standard beyond compare", but added some comments which are very relevant to any history of RAF navigation:-

"The embryonic treatment of air navigation reflected the common oversight of this vital activity by the RAF – a defect that was not very obvious to us in 1933. Recognition of the dire consequences of such neglect was unfortunately still light years away. Little did we know that there was then only 14 navigationally-conscious staff officers in the entire Service and their influence was accordingly minimal".

Dickie passed out top of his course and was posted to the prestigious No. 216 bomber/transport squadron, which flew Vickers Victorias from Heliopolis near Cairo. Again, when describing their operations, he has some pertinent comments:-

"Like almost everywhere else in the Service overseas, the importance of air navigation failed to be properly appreciated owing to the prevailing excellent visibility. The one serious navigator in No. 216 Sqn, Sqn Ldr Philip Mackworth, was quietly and unkindly dubbed 'a bit of an old woman' because he tried hard to improve the squadron's primitive navigation practices when most of his colleagues thought they were good enough".

It was Dickie's arrival at Manston in August 1937 at the School of Air Navigation which not only changed the course of his career but was the start of his contribution to RAF navigational history.

Dickie was on a three-month 'short' navigation course, followed by six months on the advanced course to qualify for a career commission. His course senior instructor was Flt Lt Wilf Oulton, who later had a distinguished and highly decorated career in the anti-U-boat war and as Air Vice-Marshal Oulton commanded the Grapple thermonuclear test in the pacific in 1957.

Fg Off Richardson realised his limitations when he got to Manston:

"My eyes were open when, despite having thumbed my way for four years around some of the wilder parts of the Middle East and a fairish part of untrodden Africa, the three-month preliminary navigation course disclosed [that] I scarcely knew anything about the theory of air navigation and . . . very little about its proper application".

The extinct Air Observer, phased out in 1918 – wearing the distinctive badge of a single wing sprouting from an O, was revived in late 1937, though it took another year to recruit and train them before they could reach squadrons – where they were poorly received; and for lack of qualified RAF navigation instructors, retired mercantile marine officers were recruited.

But, as Dickie recalls, "these problems were unknown to us in 1937 when we assembled at Manston to begin our laborious climb through the higher mathematics and sciences that underpin the mysteries of air navigation". Some members of the course had been pilots in flying-boat squadrons and "were well versed in coping with our elementary navigation exercises of long flights over the sea to find distant lightships in the North Sea and the Channel".

The 'long' six-month air navigation course followed in January 1938 and – as Dickie remembered— "we had to make great efforts to keep up with our tutorials while coping with the intensive flying schedule in fair weather and foul".

"The comforts of Manston compensated for some extremely 'hairy' night flights, navigating through continuous ice-forming cloud over Scotland, with the threat of fog back at base and only poor radio aids to help. Manston had no homing device except for a coded flashing light beacon on the airfield – if it could be seen".

Dickie came out second at the end of the course and – like all its members – was annotated 'N' in the Air Force List, he and his close friend Thomas L Moseley, who was top, being recruited as new instructors at the expanding School.

They were appointed to run 'Short N' courses and to modernise the syllabus for the doubling of the School's output. After two such courses they handed over to the brightest pair of Spec Ns, while they themselves were asked to run the next Specialist course and to revise its syllabus. This latter task – in Dickie's words – "involved writing memoranda and monographs on various aspects of air navigation, scribblings which were shortly to have quite unforeseen consequences for me".

It is significant that the AOC-in-C Bomber Command, Air Chief Marshal Sir Edgar Ludlow-Hewitt, at the instigation of his navigation staff – in Dickie's words – "thought it propitious for as many commanders of his squadrons and flights as possible to be indoctrinated into the latest processes of air navigation . . .

"A series of highly concentrated astro courses were at once organised at Manston for dozens of navigationally illiterate wing commanders and squadron leaders, in fortnightly batches. To reach clear night skies often meant flying Ansons at 19,000ft. in the perishing cold without oxygen [or cabin heating]. This task was repeated again and again until the programme had been completed . . ."

Manston, however, was to be cleared for use as a forward base: the School was to move to St. Athan in South Wales and from mid-August started packing up. The move – by air and train – began on 3 September 1939 as the air raid siren wailed over Ramsgate railway station.

For Dickie Richardson the turning-point in his career came at St. Athan. Group Captain Robertson sent for him to say that a recent attempt to re-write the basic text-book on air navigation had fizzled out. As the monographs he had written for his Course "showed a gift for simplifying abstruse theories", Robbie asked if he could nominate him for this task; it would mean a back-room job for a time.

The existing manual – Air Pilotage – was outdated and its title betrayed its origins. The theory of astro navigation had been fully expounded in Air Publication 1456 by Sqn Ldr L K Barnes, but his treatise was "way above the heads of most aircrew".

There were many hurdles to surmount in mid-1940 – like operating notes on new or emerging instruments; nor did Dickie realise how long the text would take to compose; nor, when he said 'Yes' to his austere but greatly respected Group Captain, did he anticipate that Air Publication 1234 of 1941 was to "hang round his neck like a millstone for the next 17 years": nobody had warned him that it would be "potentially fatal for an RAF pilot to become type-cast as 'Mr Air Navigation' ".

At that time, Francis Chichester was writing a series of eight popular pocket-books, capitalising on his outstanding feats of solo air navigation. But "his Observer booklets fell short of the professional stance we needed in the RAF".

The recognised authority on the subject was "the excellent

Complete Air Navigator by D C T Bennett". This 1935 publication had been acclaimed as the world's best manual for civil aviation use; but by 1940 it had already only a passing relevance to the indoctrination of RAF aircrew. Dickie commented retrospectively:-

"Neither of these authors had the advantage of the very latest RAF-informed air navigation ideas, nor of our planned instrument development. Neither . . . had had to ponder the problems imposed by an enormous training plan, nor to foresee the limitations imposed by war on the practice of air navigation. My captive readership was to be vast: 125,000 HMSO copies in the UK, countless reprints in the Dominions and translations for the Czech, Polish and Norwegian Air Forces. Even the Chinese had one . . . Who was to guess that the Germans would make a translation by 1943?"

Dickie asked to be sent to London. Blitz or no Blitz, he "had to be near the people who mattered"; he "needed to know . . . what was going on, not only in the squadrons but also in technical developments which had begun to take off in all directions".

In London he was "given a navigation niche in the Training Department of the Air Ministry, ostensibly for writing but he soon became lumbered by other duties". He had a fourth-floor office in Adastral House in Kingsway.

In order to taste real life with the operational squadrons he flew up to Wyton, where a Spec N contemporary, Wg Cdr Paul Wood DFC, commanded a Wellington squadron. Then he went up to the bomber station at Driffield to make contacts there. These 1940-41 winter visits gave him "a very faint insight" into what Bomber Command was doing. It was not then known, he recalled, that "despite all their training, courage and determination, the air navigators . . . were so ill-equipped for their difficult operational task as to be lamentably ineffective".

His next priority as to ascertain what the 'boffins' had in store – his quest beginning with the officers who framed the Operational Requirements, notably OR3 in Richmond Terrace headed by Wg Cdr David J Waghorn DFC (brother of the Schneider Trophy winner) and of whom Francis Chichester wrote that he had "the exceptional and most valuable combination of originality in devising methods of navigation and a keep practical sense of what is required and feasible in the air".

David Waghorn welcomed Dickie to his "holy of holies" in

Whitehall and carefully monitored the information he was collecting about the shape of things to come: he was "a most important yard-arm" and only after several discussions did Dickie fell confident to proceed.

Initially Dickie was in an Assistant Directorate headed by a "friendly, laid-back" Wing Commander Gareth G Barrett, who when it was upgraded to a Deputy Directorate was posted to command No. 210 Catalina Sqn. at Oban and replaced by L 'Kelly' Barnes – "a very dynamic Group Captain, recognised as probably the most erudite air navigation specialist then alive in the RAF and even in the world".

In the 1940-41 winter they were joined by Flt Lt Frank Chichester, then nursing a duodenal ulcer by constantly sipping milk and munching digestive biscuits, later Sir Francis for his outstanding feats of air and sea navigation, with whom Dickie formed a lifelong friendship and of whom he recalled:-

"Frank and I had our say in helping to re-shape the layout and contents of the Air Almanac, AP1602, that remarkable joint brainchild of Kelly and . . . Dr D H Sadler OBE, the brilliant Royal Observatory astronomer and Superintendent of the Nautical Almanac – a genius of great modesty. The Air Almanac was the foundation for the revolution in astro navigation . . ."

By the end of May 1941 Dickie had finished the first six chapters – which dealt with the basics of navigation terminology. He had developed close contacts with S5(b), the Air Ministry secretariat which liaised with HMSO for publications. They fell in with his plans for multi-coloured diagrams and text and didn't jib at his request for a normally bound quarto hardback – instead of the "stereotyped official publication held together by boot laces". He was given a call on the services of their professional draughtsmen to polish up his rough diagrams which formed the majority of the Manual's 233 illustrations; and his need for specially miniaturised maps presented no problem.

Dickie recalls that he was glad to be able to include the eagerly awaited Astrograph, an invention of Pritchard and Lamplough from RAE Farnborough – "on which we were pinning such high hopes of simplifying and thereby enhancing the operational use of astro". He assigned a photograph showing an Astrograph in a mock-up over a navigation table as "the most prestigious frontispiece" for the Manual.

In these last stages of gestation he recalled a book on banking which he had read in 1928 for his BCom degree, which used Lewis Carroll quotations as chapter headings: he decided to cull 12 from "Alice" and "The Hunting of the Snark". In a 1991 RAF Historical Society lecture at the RAF Museum former Luftwaffe Condor captain/navigator Dr Karl Karwarth related how he had been asked to translate a captured copy of AP1234 and that the only parts which defeated him were the Lewis Carroll quotations.

On 6 June 1941 Dickie Richardson announced the arrival of the first 50,000 copies in a Memo to his T Nav colleagues. An advance copy with its 817 paragraphs in 328 pages reached him in late August. First 'pulls' from the presses were rushed to Canada, South Africa, Australia and New Zealand to local presses, to copy and publish as required.

Dickie's promotion to Wing Commander came through in September 1941 and he was invited by his former colleague 'Gee Gee' Barrett to fly on a maritime sortie with No. 210 Catalina Sqn. from Oban. It was on this trip that he conceived the idea of another of his contributions to RAF navigation – noticing that there were two pilots with 'George' but only one navigator on a 15hr trip, so pressing for a limit of 10 hours on a navigator's tour of duty.

He himself was now bound for maritime operations – in command of No. 502 (AuxAF) Sqn. of Whitleys at Limavady – preceded by No. 3 OTU at Cranwell, where the six-week course was pared down to 11 days because he was urgently needed at Limavady.

He left his command in September 1942 to become Chief Navigation Officer at Coastal Command HQ – "perhaps thanks to a reputation as the author of AP1234 which was being widely acclaimed". At the HQ at Northwood, Middlesex, he "set about creating a properly balanced Navigation team, headed by a Group Captain . . ."

On 1 February 1943 he became a paid acting Group Captain.

His plans included the fitting of the Distant Reading Compass (or its American equivalent) in all maritime aircraft. For the Leigh Light Wellingtons the AYF radio altimeter was absolutely essential for safe descent to 15ft asl in all weather conditions and at night. All CC aircraft desperately needed an improved drift sight which would have to be optically periscopic. As soon as they became available, the Air Mileage Unit and Air Position Indicator would become other top priorities for maritime aircraft. Above all, Dickie was "determined to get the Top Secret electronic fixing aid which was on the point of general issue to Bomber Command. Called GEE, it gave the bomber navigators invaluable coverage eastwards over Europe as far as the Ruhr and was potentially useful for our North Sea strike squadrons. Unfortunately it did not extend to the south-west, where the existing radio was useless. We badly needed GEE in the Bay but that would involve an entirely new GEE chain being set up on new sites in the south-west".

He attended a meeting in London called (he thought) by Sir Robert Renwick himself to sponsor a new GEE chain in the south-west. "Little did I then visualise how vital that SW GEE chain would become for our patrols protecting the Overlord invasion fleets in June 1944".

An in-house monthly Coastal Command Newsletter was launched, which "helped to create a sense of professional concern and pride among the navigators". One of the "innovative policies" discussed in its pages was the introduction of Second Navigators.

Dickie's next move was "to establish a qualified staff navigator at every station, from Iceland to Gibraltar and from the Shetlands to the Azores, to forge links, via the Group navigation staff, between my officers and each squadron . . . Within six weeks, a strong navigation organisation had been created".

Dickie also "contemplated the longer-term problems arising from the persistent widespread refusal to recognise the vital importance of the element of air navigation which lay at the centre of all planning and air operations. There was still a lack of focus in the higher echelons of the Air Staff when they touched on anything naviga-tional and we paid dearly for this myopia".

He introduced a systematic navigation 'Drill' throughout the Command – air navigators would have to make certain hourly observations such as regular three-course drift measurements to calculate wind velocity, to make DR as accurate as possible. Position 'fixes' had to be obtained whenever possible; the air navigators thus had a systematic routine to follow automatically. It was decided that an Air Plot should be kept as standard practice. It became necessary to monitor its adoption by squadrons in the Command. A monthly inter-squadron competition was held, results being published in the monthly Newsletter. "There had been nothing like this before, on such a large scale".

A by-product of the Drill was the evidence it produced of the effect of air navigator's fatigue, which "became startlingly apparent on sorties that regularly exceeded ten hours' duration. The air navigators of Catalinas almost always had to slog away single-handed for 15 hours in the air" (the longest recorded sortie was one of over 24 hours). "The only answer to this was the earliest possible establishment" (in 1943) "of a Second Air Navigator in all aircraft crews whose operational sorties exceeded ten hours' duration" – a "tenaciously argued" innovation.

(Note: Between 25 and 31 May, 1942, Ernest Schofield, an observer flying in Catalinas with 210 Squadron, flew three special reconnaissance missions lasting 27hrs 11mins, 24hrs 38mins, and 18hr 30mins (curtailed due to bad weather) respectively; for these sorties he was awarded the DFC).

Dickie records the first Navigator to be made an aircraft Captain – Robert Augustine Irving, at the Liberator OTU at Nassau in the Bahamas, and also the origin of Air Ministry Order No A410 of 20 May 1948, by which equal career opportunities were offered to pilots and navigators.

As a result largely of his persistence and promptings, a Directorate of Navigation was created under ACAS (Ops) in CAS's Department in June 1944.

He records the maritime air contribution to D Day, 6 June 1944 – 60 squadrons, their task "to sweep an appointed area of sea by ASV every 30 minutes, day and night, regardless of weather, starting two weeks before D Day and continuing until further notice". The area to be covered totalled 50,000 square miles.

Operation Cork, with its 12 interlocking boxes, was a brilliant success: Dickie was angry that Sqn Ldr James Perry, who devised it, only received a MiD in the post-Overlord awards.

On 1 September 1944 Dickie left Northwood for Shawbury, to become Deputy Commandant and Director of Studies at the new Empire Air Navigation School: its Commandant was Air Cdre Philip Mackworth, with whom Dickie had served in No. 216 Sqn. The four aims of the EANS were to create a repository of aviation knowledge; to build a common forum where "air forces of the Dominions and ourselves could study and research side by side; to co-ordinate development of navigation from the user's point of view; and maintain a continuous liaison with the Dominions and Allies by frequent flying visits and by drawing staff and students from the RAF, the Dominions and Allied Air Forces". Its transPolar flights attracted widespread Press interest. Dickie went from there to Staff College on No. 16 War Course.

Humphrey Wynn

Group Captain Richardson at a Graduation Parade, June 1954

Royal Air Force Historical Society

The Royal Air Force has been in existence for over 75 years; the study of its history is deepening, and continues to be the subject of published works of consequence. Fresh attention is being given to the strategic assumptions under which military air power was first created and which largely determined policy and operations in both World Wars, the inter-war period, and in the era of Cold War tension. Material dealing with post-war history is now becoming available under the 30-year rule. These studies are important to academic historians and to the present and future members of the RAF.

The RAF Historical Society was formed in 1986 to provide a focus for interest in the history of the RAF. It does so by providing a setting for lectures and seminars in which those interested in the history of the RAF have the opportunity to meet those who participated in the evolution and implementation of policy. The Society believes that these events make an important contribution to the permanent record.

The Society normally holds three lectures or seminars a year in London, with occasional events in other parts of the country. Transcripts of lectures and seminars are published in the Journal of the RAF Historical Society, which is a publication free of charge to members. Individual membership is open to all with an interest in RAF history, whether or not they were in the Service. Although the Society has the approval of the Air Force Board, it is entirely self-financing.

Membership of the Society costs £15 per annum and further details may be obtained from the Membership Secretary, Dr Jack Dunham, Silverhill House, Coombe, Wooton-under-Edge, Gloucestershire GL12 7ND (Tel: 01453-843362).